The Brunels' Tunnel

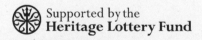
Supported by the
Heritage Lottery Fund

The most rhymed about,
danced about, sung about
and painted about
construction site
in the world

The Brunels' Tunnel

ERIC KENTLEY, ROBERT HULSE AND JULIA ELTON

FOREWORD BY MICHAEL PALIN

The Brunel Museum

This book is dedicated to the memory of
Colin James Kirkland, OBE FREng FICE, 1936–2004

A pioneering engineer in the spirit of Brunel
Chairman of Trustees, The Brunel Museum
Technical Director Channel Tunnel

First published in 2006
Second edition 2016
The Brunel Museum
Brunel Engine House
Railway Avenue
Rotherhithe
London SE16 4LF
020 7231 3840
www.brunel-museum.org.uk

Copyright © 2016
The Brunel Museum, London
Foreword © Michael Palin 2016

British Library Cataloguing-in-Publication Data
ISBN 0–9504361–2–7
ISBN 978–0–9504361–2–8

Designed by Isambard Thomas, London
Printed in Italy by Graphicom

The Brunel Museum wishes to thank the
following for their support of this publication:
Heritage Lottery Fund
The British Tunnelling Society
CH2M
Subterranea Britannica
Thames Tideway Tunnel
Mott MacDonald
The Engineering Group of the Geological Society
Institution of Civil Engineers
Sir William McAlpine
Steve Hurst
and an anonymous donor

COVER: A watercolour painted by Marc Brunel
in 1835. It is thought that the elderly figure in
the west tunnel is Marc himself, with his
daughter Sophie and her husband Benjamin
Hawes, MP, in the east tunnel. In the boat above
them is Benjamin's brother William, rowing his
friend Isambard Kingdom Brunel. On the reverse
of the watercolour, reproduced on the back of this
book, Marc drew a schematic illustration of the
strata under the river. Amongst the annotations,
in the bottom left is a comparative drawing of the
size of an earlier tunnel – Richard Trevithick's –
which never reached Wapping. The watercolour
was acquired by The Brunel Museum with the
support of The Art Fund

**The Queen's Award
for Voluntary Service**

Foreword 6

A Chronology of the Thames Tunnel 8

Under the River 11

The Remarkable Brunels 13

A Tunnel for the Thames 20

Beginning the Tunnel 26

Finishing the Tunnel 50

The Celebrated Tunnel 67

The Fate of the Tunnel 72

Where the Tunnel Led 76

The Tunnel Today 79

Bibliography 82

Acknowledgements 83

Foreword by Michael Palin

The story of Brunel's tunnel under the Thames is a fine combination of drama, farce, ingenuity, showmanship and sheer engineering chutzpah, the like of which we shall probably never see again.

In a modern world of cost-overruns and wringing of hands when any great national building is delivered a few months late, it's worth remembering that this pioneering tunnel under the Thames took over fifteen years, or almost five hundred per cent, longer to complete than had originally been estimated.

Nor can we be jingoistic about it. The tunnel's chief engineer, Marc Brunel, was a Frenchman – and his son Isambard (recently voted the second Greatest Briton in a BBC poll) was an Anglo-French co-production if ever there was one; the son of a French lieutenant and an English governess, Sophia Kingdom.

Isambard Kingdom went on to eclipse his father with his inspired engineering works on the Great Western Railway, but the Thames Tunnel was the crowning glory of Brunel Senior. He it was who came up with the idea of using a steel case as a tunnel-boring shield, a method since adopted and used in all the great underground boring projects nearly two hundred years later.

Isambard joined his father Marc on the project a year after the tunnellers first went down. It was 1826 and Brunel Junior was just out of his teens.

Nothing was easy at the time. There were constant problems including unhealthy working conditions and the alarming inability of the tunnel to keep out water. Nowadays Health and Safety would have cleared the area for miles around, but the Brunels' answer to the recurrent flooding was to throw a party, inside the tunnel itself – a sit-down banquet complete with candelabra, cut-glass and the Coldstream Guards. This has been immortalised in the atmospheric, almost surreal painting by George Jones, and just as well, for otherwise we'd surely not believe it. Audacity and lunatic optimism continued to characterise progress over the next seventeen years until in 1843 the first Londoners were able to walk from one side of the city to the other, beneath their river. How heroic that must have seemed.

When the railways came in the 1860s pedestrian access was sacrificed to the new and much more commercial technology and to this day The Thames Tunnel is still used as a vital part of London's great transport system.

The Brunel brand could be characterised by innovation, technical challenge, flair and practicality, but they also had an acute marketing sense. Marc Brunel knew that everything had to be done to coax the public down into this strange, somewhat threatening subterranean world, described by the actress Fanny Kemble when she visited in 1827, as "like one of the long avenues of light that lead to the abodes of the genii in fairy tales".

So they built a shopping arcade under the Thames and in 1852 an underwater fair, where by the light of Boggett's patent Prismatic Reflectors visitors could enjoy watching Mr. Green the celebrated Bottle Pantomimic Equilibrist or dancing to music of the Montreal Minstrels in a Ballroom 150 feet long.

This great underwater crossing was a feat of engineering which the Victorians, never short on hyperbole, called the Eighth Wonder Of The World. Its continued use today as part of the East London Line is testimony to the far-sighted technical skill of Marc and Isambard Brunel. What we shouldn't forget is the grip that the Thames Tunnel had on the popular imagination at the time; a combination of joy, pleasure, wonder and sheer excitement, which is not dead and which echoes up from the riverbed to this day.

The Thames Tunnel, the first of an underground network that transformed our city's life is something of which Londoners always were, and should always remain, rightly proud.

MICHAEL PALIN, London, March 2006

A Chronology of the Thames Tunnel

1798

Ralph Dodd's attempt at a tunnel between Gravesend and Tilbury fails.

1802

Robert Vazie proposes a tunnel between Rotherhithe and Limehouse.

1805

The newly-formed Thames Archway Company is empowered to undertake the project.

1807 AUGUST

Vazie begins his tunnel.

1808 JANUARY

This tunnel is flooded just less than 200 ft short of completion and is abandoned.

1818

Marc Brunel patents a device for 'Forming Drifts and Tunnels Under Ground'.

1821

Marc is imprisoned for debt.

1824 FEBRUARY

Marc creates great enthusiasm for the idea of a tunnel when he gives a lecture to the Institution of Civil Engineers.

MARCH

Marc enlists the support of the Duke of Wellington.

JUNE

The parliamentary Bill defining the powers of the Thames Tunnel Company for 'Making and Maintaining a Tunnel under the Thames' receives the Royal Assent.

1825 MARCH

The formal opening of work on the shaft at Rotherhithe takes place.

JUNE

The top of the brick tower is sunk below ground level.

NOVEMBER

The boring of the tunnel begins.

1827 JANUARY

Isambard Brunel, who has been acting as resident engineer for several months, is officially confirmed in the appointment.

MAY

Protesting about cuts in their wages, the miners go on strike. The first major flood. The tunnel is 549 ft long.

AUGUST

Marc suffers a paralytic stroke.

NOVEMBER

The celebration banquet takes place in the tunnel. Work begins again.

1828 JANUARY

Second major flood. Six men are killed and Isambard is injured. The tunnel is 605 ft long.

FEBRUARY

Isambard suffers the first of a series of haemorrhages and is laid up for several months.

AUGUST

The tunnel is bricked up after a new issue of shares fails to raise adequate money.

1834 APRIL

The Tunnel Club is founded by Fellows of Royal Society at the Spreadeagle & Crown inn (now the Mayflower) opposite the tunnel works on Marc Brunel's 65th birthday.

DECEMBER

The first part of a £270,000 loan from the Treasury is made over to the Thames Tunnel Company.

1835 MARCH
The new shield is installed underground and tunnelling restarts.

1837 AUGUST
Third major flood. The tunnel is 736 ft long.
NOVEMBER
Fourth major flood. One miner is killed. The tunnel is
742 ft long.

1838 MARCH
Fifth major flood. The tunnel is 763 ft long.

1839 AUGUST
The tunnel reaches the low-water mark on the Wapping shore.

1840 MARCH
Marc is knighted by Queen Victoria.
JUNE
Marc takes possession of the land for the Wapping shaft.

1841 NOVEMBER
The tunnel reaches the Wapping shaft.

1843 MARCH
The Thames Tunnel is opened to pedestrian traffic.
It is 1,200 ft long.
JULY
Queen Victoria visits the tunnel.

1852
The first Thames Tunnel Fancy Fair is held.

1865 SEPTEMBER
The tunnel is formally handed over to the East London Railway.

1869 DECEMBER
The first passenger train on the East London Railway passes
through the tunnel.

1973
A charity is established to restore the old engine house, by now a
scheduled Ancient Monument.

1980
The restored building is opened to the public as the Brunel Engine
House Museum.

1993
Thames Tunnel designated International Civil Engineering
landmark

2002
The Museum earns the Freedom of the Ancient Metropolitan
Borough of Bermondsey, a civic award for services to the
community.

2005
The Museum achieves the status of a Registered Museum and
changes its name to The Brunel Museum.

2006
Just before the bicentennial of Isambard Kingdom Brunel's birth,
the Museum welcomes its 50,000th visitor.

2010
Museum given Queen's Award for Voluntary Service.

2012
Thames Tunnel Walking Tours before re-opening as London
Overground, an orbital railway.

2016
Sinking shaft re-opened by Prince Edward, Earl of Wessex as the
Grand Entrance Hall, a gallery and performance space and
National Historic Landmark.

Under the River

But I must tell you what this tunnel is like, or at least try to do so. You enter, by flights of stairs, the first door, and find yourself on a circular platform, which surrounds the top of a well or shaft, of about two hundred feet in circumference and five hundred in depth. This well is an immense iron frame of cylindrical form, filled in with bricks; it was constructed on level ground, and then, by some wonderful mechanical process, sunk into the earth. In the midst of this is a steam engine, and above, or below, as far as your eye can see, huge arms are working up and down while the creaking, crashing, whirring noises, and the swift whirling of innumerable wheels all around you, make you feel for the first few minutes as if you were going distracted. I should have liked to look much longer at all these beautiful, wise, working creatures …

On turning round at the foot of the last flight of steps through an immense dark arch, as far as sight could reach stretched a vaulted passage, smooth earth underfoot, the white arches of the roof beyond, the whole lighted by a line of gas lamps, and as bright, almost, as if it were broad day. It was like one of the long avenues of light that lead to the abodes of the genii in fairy tales. The profound stillness of the place, first broken by my father's voice, to which the vaulted roof gave extraordinary and startling volume of tone, the indescribable feeling of subterranean vastness, the amazement and delight I experienced, quite overcame me, and I was obliged to turn from the friend who was explaining everything to me, to cry and ponder in silence.

Mr Brunel, who was superintending some of the works, came to my father and offered to conduct us to where the workmen were employed – an unusual favour, which of course delighted us all. So we left our broad, smooth path of light, and got into dark passages, where we stumbled among coils of ropes and heaps of pipes and piles of planks, and where ground springs were welling up and flowing about in every direction. An iron frame has been constructed – a sort of cage, divided into many compartments, in each of which a man with his lantern and his tools is placed – and

The tunnellers at work by
Edmund Marks, 1835

as they clear the earth away this iron frame is moved onward and advances into new ground. The appearance of the work-men themselves, all begrimed, with their brawny arms and legs bare, some standing in black water up to their knees, with the red, murky light of links and lanterns flashing and flickering about them, made a most striking picture.

As we returned I remained at the bottom of the stairs last of all, to look back at the beautiful road to Hades, wishing I might be left behind...'

The eighteen-year old Fanny Kemble, later to become the most celebrated actress of her generation, wrote these words in 1827. She is describing one of the marvels – although not yet complete – of the early nineteenth century: the first tunnel ever successfully dug under a river.

Over a century and a half later, fourteen million people pass through this tunnel every year. Yet most of the travellers on London Transport's East London underground line between Rotherhithe and Wapping will barely notice when the train dips to pass under the Thames. Fewer still will be aware that the darkness conceals the arches and pillars of one of the most important structures in engineering history. But they are travelling through a truly incredible feat of engineering: a tunnel which should be celebrated not simply for being the first, but also because it is a story of remarkable ingenuity coupled with dogged persistence; because the techniques of tunnelling pioneered here were still in use in the late 20th century for the digging of the Channel Tunnel; and because, although it came close to killing him, the Thames Tunnel can be said to have launched the career of Britain's greatest civil engineer – Isambard Kingdom Brunel.

The Remarkable Brunels

The legacy of Isambard Kingdom Brunel still marks the landscape of England and Wales, from the railway lines of Cornwall to the relics on the Thames foreshore of the launchways of his last steamship, the *Great Eastern*. The boldness of his vision and enterprise has made him the most famous of all the remarkable Victorian engineers, but an inadvertent consequence has been that his achievements have overshadowed, almost to the point of invisibility, the achievements of his father, Marc Isambard Brunel. Yet Marc was one of the greatest civil and mechanical engineers of the late 18th-/early 19th centuries, a man of even greater inventive genius than his son. And his life was even more adventurous.

THE YOUNG MARC BRUNEL

Born on 25th April 1769 in the family farmhouse at Hacqueville near Etrepagny in Normandy, Marc showed an intuitive understanding of mechanical devices from an early age. While still a small child, he designed and constructed a musical machine that combined the sound of flute and harpsichord. Asked by his father 'what do you want to be?' Marc replied 'an engineer', a response puzzling to an eighteenth-century gentleman farmer. As a second son, he was expected to enter the Church or the Law. But after two years in a seminary from the age of eleven, the priests were convinced that, despite his talents and sunny temperament, a career in the Church was not for him.

His prospects would have been bleak had it not been for a fortunate family connection. The Brunels were closely related to the Carpentier family, amongst whose friends was Vincent Dulague, Professor of Hydrography at the Royal College of Rouen. Dulague agreed to tutor Marc for entry to the French Navy as an officer cadet. Marc was now in his element, soaking up knowledge from the professor and in his spare time producing detailed architectural sketches of the major buildings of Rouen. Dulague was so impressed with his pupil that in due course he persuaded Louis XVI's Minister of Marine to appoint him as a junior officer on a new corvette. In 1786 the

Maréchal de Castries sailed from Rouen with the seventeen year-old on board. Typically, he carried with him his own hand-made navigator's quadrant, which he was to use throughout his naval career.

This was to last less than six years, for in January 1792, the *Maréchal de Castries* returned to Rouen and her crew was paid off. Marc disembarked to find his country dramatically transformed: the French Revolution was in its third year.

THE FLIGHT TO SAFETY

Marc was a royalist and his views were soon to get him into trouble. In January 1793 he was in the Café de l'Échelle in Paris with his friend, François Carpentier, where he unwisely predicted the downfall of the Revolution's leader, Robespierre. The incensed clientele attempted to seize them, but luckily Marc and François managed to escape, hiding in a nearby inn until nightfall before returning to the Carpentier residence in Rouen.

It was here that Marc met a young English girl. Some weeks earlier, the seventeen year-old Sophia Kingdom had arrived in France to learn the language, accompanied by two friends, a Frenchman and his English wife. But the country was in turmoil, and the friends decided to return to England. Unfortunately, Sophia had fallen ill, too ill to travel, so it was decided that she would remain with the Carpentiers. It was not long before she and Marc fell in love.

However, Rouen, once a royalist enclave, was now firmly in the hands of the revolutionaries and Marc and Sophia were forced into hiding. Marc's friends managed to obtain a passport for him and permission to travel to America, ostensibly to purchase grain for the French Navy. Leaving Sophia behind, he sailed on board the aptly named *Liberty*, arriving in New York in September 1793. Meanwhile, back in Rouen, Sophia was arrested as an enemy alien and incarcerated in a makeshift prison in Gravelines. She was to remain there until July 1794, when, with Robespierre's fall, she was suddenly released. Somehow, the nineteen year-old girl, ill and emaciated, made her way back to Rouen. The Carpentiers nursed her back to health and in the following year Sophia obtained a passport and returned to England.

AMERICAN CITIZEN

In exile on the other side of the Atlantic, Marc soon established a considerable reputation within the engineering community in the USA. When he was still only

twenty-six, he managed to persuade a wealthy New York merchant called Thurman to back a project to cut a canal linking the Hudson River with Lake Champlain, thereby linking New York and the St Lawrence River. This was one of the first great canals of North America. Marc also entered a competition for the design of a new Capitol building which was judged the best entry. Although too costly to build, a modified version of the design was used for a theatre in the Bowery.

In the autumn of 1796, Marc, now an American citizen, was appointed Chief Engineer of New York. In this role he undertook many building and engineering projects, including an innovative cannon foundry. Some two years after his appointment he was at a dinner where the conversation turned to the political situation in Europe – specifically Napoleon's imperial ambitions and the impending conflict with Britain's Royal Navy. One of the guests, a fellow Frenchman, pointed out that one of the Royal Navy's major supply problems was a shortage of the rigging blocks that the sailing ships used in large quantities. The Navy needed 100,000 blocks a year and the laborious hand-carving process could not keep up with the demand. Marc quickly realised the commercial possibilities of a more efficient production method.

His inventive mind went to work and he designed a set of machines to automate the production of blocks, and in February 1799 he sailed for England to find his fortune – and to find Sophia Kingdom, and marry her before the year was out.

ENGLAND

Indeed, within days of arriving in London, Marc and Sophia were reunited and engaged to be married. A month later, he filed the first of his many patent specifications – not for a block-making machine but for a 'Duplicate Writing and Drawing Machine', described by Marc as a 'polygraph' which consisted of linked quill pens arranged so that up to three copies of a letter or report could be made while the original was being written.

But the block-making machine was still his prime concern and, in pursuit of producing working models from drawings, he was fortunate to find Henry Maudslay. At the dawn of an age which saw the world transformed by the power of machines, Maudslay was a pivotal figure. He was virtually the founder of the machine-tool industry and devices such as the screw cutting lathe, the planing machine and the micrometer all emerged from his workshop in London's Wells Street. In 1801 Marc filed his patent, which described '*A New and Useful Machine for Cutting One or More Mortices, Forming the Sides of and Cutting the Pin Hole of the Shells of Blocks and for Turning and Boring the Shivers, and Fitting and Fixing the Coak Therein'*.

Despite being armed with Maudslay's models, Marc was robustly rebuffed by the Navy's principal supplier of blocks, Fox & Taylor. Samuel Taylor (son of founder Walter Taylor) wrote to Marc, saying of Walter's block-making techniques, '. . . I have no hope of anything ever better being discovered and I am convinced there cannot. At the present time, were we ever so inclined, we could not attempt any alteration ...' Undismayed, Marc successfully lobbied higher up the chain of procurement and in April 1802 the Inspector General of Naval Works recommended that the new block-making machines be installed at Portsmouth Dockyard.

Marc's financial reward was to be a sum equal to the savings resulting from one year's full-scale operation of the plant, plus an allowance of one guinea a day – but this did not bring him financial security. He had paid Maudslay for the models himself as well as the cost of developing the special saws needed. The Navy Board procrastinated over payment and it was to take nine years of acrimonious argument for him to receive his full payment. Meanwhile, he had a growing family to support – and on 9th April 1806 Sophia gave birth to their third child, a boy, whom they named Isambard Kingdom Brunel.

Yet Marc's inventive genius was undiminished. In 1809 he happened to see some of the returning veterans from the Battle of Corunna and was shocked by the sight of their unshod, lacerated feet, bandaged with rags. Apparently, faulty boots, which began to break up on the first day's march, caused as many casualties as enemy action. Marc promptly designed a superior boot and the machines to make them. After his experience with the Navy, he decided on a private venture and set up a factory employing twenty-four disabled soldiers to produce good, strong boots and shoes in nine different sizes. They were such a success that in 1812, the Foreign Secretary, Lord Castlereagh, persuaded him to expand production to supply all the Army's needs.

Then things went disastrously wrong. In 1814 the boot factory was destroyed by fire, and the following year the peace with France following the Battle of Waterloo brought an abrupt end to purchases from the Army, leaving him with large stocks of unwanted boots. By 1820, his other business enterprises were also ailing, then in 1821 his bankers, Sykes and Company, became insolvent. Creditors turned on him. In May 1821 Marc and Sophia were arrested for debt and consigned to the King's Bench Prison.

Marc continued to work from prison and to write to friends and business contacts. These included Alexander I, Tsar of Russia, who in 1817 had commissioned Marc to design a bridge for the Neva at St Petersburg (although it was never built). It was rumoured that Marc was considering leaving England for Russia and the matter of retaining his services in England suddenly became an issue of national concern. The Duke of Wellington and the prime minister intervened on Marc's behalf and consequently the Government offered £5,000 to pay off his creditors. In August, after three months in prison, Marc and Sophia were freed. However, the thinking work on his next and greatest project, a tunnel under the Thames, had already begun.

HIS FATHER'S SON – ISAMBARD KINGDOM BRUNEL

Despite Marc's remarkable contribution to industrial production, the title of Britain's most famous engineer must surely go to his son, Isambard. His achievements have been widely and rightly celebrated, but the enterprise which launched his career – perversely by almost costing him his life – was his father's greatest project, the Thames Tunnel.

Although born in Portsea, Isambard was really a Londoner, having been taken there in 1807 when Marc moved the family to Chelsea. Tutored initially by Marc, Isambard was eventually sent to a boarding school in Hove. Finishing there in 1814, he was now sent to France to gain what was unobtainable in England – a technical education. After a time at Caen College he studied at the Lycée Henri IV in Paris, in preparation for the École Polytechnique. Unfortunately, his English birth barred him from entry to the latter institution and instead he was apprenticed to the famous watchmaker Louis Breguet. Returning home in August 1822, he immediately joined his father's drawing office. He was set to work designing bridges for London and Liverpool and on a commission from the Admiralty to develop the practical application of condensed gases – a 'Gaz' engine, designed to run on carbonic gas, one of the few Brunel projects that was to prove a complete failure.

Isambard Kingdom Brunel by his brother-in-law John Horsley, 1857

A Tunnel for the Thames

LONDON'S CROSSINGS

London Bridge was first built in the twelfth century and until 1750 was the only bridge crossing the Thames in London. The only alternative means of transporting people and goods was by boat. The carriageway across the bridge was flanked by buildings, but even though these were swept away around 1760 to increase the width of the road, it did little to ease the congestion. Several new bridges were built – despite the opposition of the watermen – during the second half of the eighteenth century – Westminster Bridge (1750), Kew Bridge (1759), Blackfriars (1769 and originally called Pitt Bridge, after the Earl of Chatham), Battersea (1771) and, further upriver, Richmond (1777). Yet of all these, only Blackfriars was close enough to provide relief to the congestion on London Bridge. Even the bridges added in the early years of the nineteenth century – Vauxhall Bridge (1816), Waterloo Bridge (1817) and Southwark Bridge (1819) – while serving the growing needs of people working and living to the west of the City – gave little relief to the two bridges which had to carry the traffic of the port and City of London in the east.

THE DEVELOPING DOCKS

Up until the beginning of the nineteenth century, merchant ships coming into London could only unload at the quays between the Tower of London and London Bridge. The concentration of vessels here meant that ships could be moored in the river for three months waiting for their cargoes to be unloaded. This chaotic arrangement also encouraged serious theft: the waiting ships were easy prey for gangs who cut them from their moorings under cover of darkness – often with the help of the crew – and raided them when they ran aground.

In 1802 the West India merchants opened the first enclosed docks at the northern end of the Isle of Dogs. These provided berths for six hundred ships and, with high walls and armed guards, the docks successfully reduced the losses from river thieves and guaranteed the payment of customs dues. Other enclosed docks soon followed: the London Docks at Wapping, the East India Docks at Blackwall and the Surrey Docks, all built in the first years of the nineteenth century.

What this rapid development of the docks meant was that London quickly became the largest and most advanced port in Europe but the nearest river crossing was still London Bridge, by now very old and as much as four miles away from the new docks. Even when the bridge was reached, the crossing was slow, as an estimated four thousand vehicles struggled across the bridge every day.

Meanwhile many people relied on the Thames watermen to ferry them across the river, with up to three hundred and fifty of them working every day.

There was therefore a very strong commercial case for another Thames crossing to the east of London Bridge. And there was also a strategic case. In 1798, Ralph Dodd, the engineer who built the Grand Surrey Canal, had published a paper in which he wrote: 'In the course of my professional travelling, I have observed the want of a grand uninterrupted line of communication in the south-east part of the Kingdom, which could easily be obtained if the River Thames could be conveniently passed.' Importantly, the army would find it far easier to repel invaders if it could reach the south and east coasts without being funnelled over one of the bridges in the middle of the city. This military consideration was to be an important factor in the decisive support which the Duke of Wellington would give to the eventual completion of the project which promised the solution.

There were however immediate technical problems. Any bridge would have to be high enough for tall ships' masts to pass underneath so that the quays by the Tower could be reached, so not only would the structure be enormous but would need very long approach roads. It would be hugely expensive. Although bascule bridges – similar in principle to the later Tower Bridge – were familiar in Europe, steam-engines at that time were not sufficiently advanced to cope with lifting bascules of the weight that the width of the Thames demanded. Furthermore, such a bridge would have to be raised so frequently to allow ships to pass that it would hardly be a continuous crossing for wheeled traffic.

The alternative was a tunnel. But a tunnel through 'soft ground' like that under the Thames did not exist anywhere in the world. 'Soft ground' means loose, uncompressed material such as gravel, sand or mud. Unlike rock, which is rigid, soft ground by its nature collapses if not supported from below. The problems are worse

Nineteenth-century congestion

PREVIOUS PAGES
The Thames from the Surrey side
showing ships waiting to be unloaded
and the newly built London Docks, by
William Daniell, 1803

underneath a river because there, the loose material is under downward pressure from the water above, which would swiftly surge through in the event of a collapse.

Tunnels under rivers were not unknown. In the ancient world, the Assyrian Queen Semiramis contributed considerably to her own legend by having the River Euphrates at Babylon diverted while a tunnel for her personal use was built underneath it; and the Romans were said to have tunnelled under the sea off the French port of Marseille. In the modern era there were some underwater mine workings in Cornwall and at the turn of the nineteenth century a tunnel had been cut beneath the estuary of the River Tyne on the northeast coast. This too, however, was an adjunct to a mine and had been cut through rock. No-one had yet successfully tunnelled under soft ground.

EARLIER TUNNELS UNDER THE THAMES

Ralph Dodd drew up plans for a 900-yard tunnel further down river between Gravesend and Tilbury. He sank a shaft but could not find the bed of chalk that he had been counting on, and when the money he'd raised ran out the project came to an end. But in 1802 Robert Vazie, a Cornish tin mining engineer, his imagination probably fired by Dodd's efforts, proposed a much shorter tunnel between Rotherhithe and Limehouse. From a shaft sunk at Rotherhithe, Vazie planned a 'driftway' (a small pilot tunnel) 3 ft wide at the bottom, 2 ft 6 in. wide at the top and a mere 5 ft high, reinforced with a timber lining in the traditional miners' fashion. Once completed, it would act as a drain when the proper tunnel was built above it later. By 1805 the idea had raised sufficient interest and money for a 'Thames Archway Company' to be empowered by Parliament to undertake the work.

Despite being forced by his directors to accept a smaller pumping engine than he really needed and to reduce the diameter of his shaft, Vazie managed to reach a depth of 76 ft. As quicksand lay below, this was where he decided to start his tunnel. It was begun in August 1807. However, at this point his directors decided to call for outside advice, and turned to Richard Trevithick, a fellow Cornishman with a considerable engineering reputation also made in the tin mines. Trevithick, a man of strong character, was soon effectively in charge of operations and it was not long before the directors dismissed Vazie.

Under Vazie, the driftway had progressed at an average of 6 ft a day, but with Trevithick now in sole charge, it increased to more than 11 ft daily. After passing its lowest point under the middle of the river, the tunnel's ascent was countered by a descending layer of rock. The miners chiselled their way through this only to emerge into quicksand, which instantly brought water into the tunnel and the rapid collapse of the part of the roof not yet supported with timber. With an amazing calmness, the miners stayed where they were, removed the collapsed earth, repaired the hole with timber, made the necessary arrangements for drainage, and continued their work. Similar incidents recurred but by January 1808 they reached the low-tide mark on the north bank of the Thames. Then, at high tide on the 26th, quicksand and water suddenly poured in through the workface. The miners had no alternative this time but to run for their lives, more than three hundred yards along the cramped, pitch-black tunnel. Trevithick was the last to leave, emerging from the tunnel with water up to his neck.

His enthusiasm unimpaired, Trevithick dumped clay onto the riverbed to seal the breach, pumped the tunnel dry and had the miners back at work a week after the inundation. Realising, however, that the riverbed was presenting more permanent problems, he now proposed to excavate the remainder of the tunnel from above: the miners would work inside a series of coffer dams digging a trench and laying a tunnel composed of cast-iron sections, like a giant pipeline, inside it.

But this was an untested idea, and Trevithick's directors preferred to offer £500 to anyone who could devise a credible alternative scheme for completing the driftway. Of the forty-nine suggestions, none was considered workable and the judges, Dr Charles Hutton and William Jessop, declared: 'Though we cannot presume to set limits to the ingenuity of other men, we must confess that under the circumstances which have been so clearly presented to us, we consider that an underground tunnel which would be useful to the public and beneficial to the adventurers is impracticable.' The tunnel, with less than 200 ft to go out of a total of 1,200 ft, was abandoned and the Thames Archway Company came to the end of its brief existence.

History has proved that Trevithick's plan for completing the tunnel would have worked: the San Francisco's Bay Area Rapid Transit Tunnel is just one example of how, years later, his far-sighted idea has been applied. But the failure of his tunnel – or rather the failure of his company directors to enable him to complete it – meant that neither the driftway method nor the excavation from above would be likely to gain financial support. An entirely new approach was needed. And this is just what Marc Brunel came up with — a completely new technique for coping with the problems of 'soft ground', for which succeeding generations of tunnelling engineers would pay him tribute.

Beginning the Tunnel

Marc had actually thought of a tunnel rather than a bridge for his River Neva project, and although he abandoned it in favour of a bridge design, his ideas for it, together with his observations on Trevithick's attempt, led him to patent a device for 'Forming Drifts and Tunnels Under Ground' in 1818.

Marc's inspiration was the shipworm, *Teredo navalis*, which bores into ships' timbers, the results of whose work he had seen while working in Chatham Dockyard. Digging with the shell-like protrusions on either side of its head, the shipworm excretes the excavated wood out of its body, using it to line and reinforce the tunnel as it moves along. This was the basis for the idea of a shield. In one version it was an iron cylinder with long rotating blades at the front to excavate the earth, the whole thing to be pushed forward, as the excavation progressed, by devices called 'hydraulic jacks'. The earth removed would be passed back through the machine and the cylinder would support the top and sides of the tunnel until a permanent brick lining had been built. But Marc soon realised that there was no steam-engine which could satisfactorily drive the blades round, and manpower was not sufficient. Furthermore, for a shield which was to hold workmen, a rectangular shape would be more practical than a round one.

He came to prefer his alternative proposal: here the shield was an iron frame facing the direction of the tunnel and containing a large number of adjacent cells, all in contact with the tunnel face. Each cell was occupied by a single miner, working independently of the others. The area of the tunnel face covered by a miner's cell was itself divided up into small areas, each covered by a removable board – a 'poling board'. A miner would remove one board at a time only, dig out the small area of the tunnel face behind it to a depth of several inches, then replace the board and do likewise with the one next to it, and so on. When a miner had excavated his part of the face, his cell would be propelled forward a few inches by the jacks at the rear of the shield.

The concept of the travelling shield is still used in tunnelling today, and Marc's invention made possible not only the first tunnel anywhere through the soft earth under a riverbed but also, in a sense, every tunnel excavated under water ever since.

Even the prototype version of the shield built by Marc demonstrates advantages over the timber-prop tunnelling techniques that had been used earlier. Partitioning a large tunnel face into tiny sections enabled much larger tunnels than before to be dug through unstable material while preventing the whole face from collapsing at once. Crucially, the shield also held up the roof of the freshly excavated tunnel over the miners' heads until the bricklayers working just behind them had given it a permanent lining. Thus, the shield made the work altogether safer for those at the workface. It also kept the excavation to an exact size and shape.

FROM DRAWING BOARD TO 'THE THAMES TUNNEL COMPANY'

Marc continued to refine his great idea: instead of each cell being independent, three cells, one on top of another, were to form a vertical frame and there would be eleven frames side-by-side, forming a massive oblong shield. He also began to publicise his idea and its application to the construction of a tunnel under the Thames. He wrote an article describing the shield in the *Mechanic's Magazine* of September 1823 and prepared booklets with which to start raising parliamentary and business support for his project.

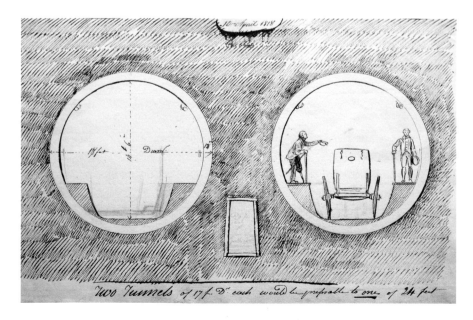

An early sketch by Marc when he was still considering a circular shield for tunnelling: note the disabled war veteran

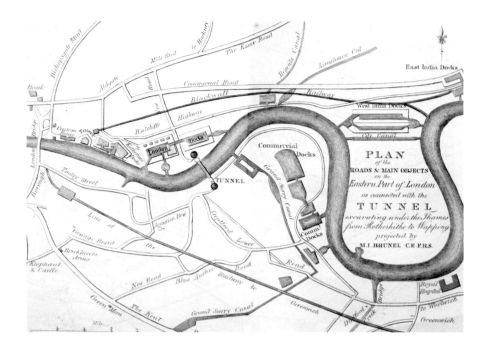

The location of the tunnel near the docks, from the guidebook to the tunnel 1843

One of the businessmen who had been involved in the defunct Thames Archway Company introduced him to William Smith, Member of Parliament for Norwich. Smith was a staunch defender of the slave trade but was nevertheless a spokesman for three Christian denominations simultaneously, and he happily added the Thames Tunnel to his interests. Marc, for his part, was happy to have Smith's parliamentary know-how at his disposal.

On 17th February 1824 Marc gave a lecture to the Institution of Civil Engineers, and as a consequence the following day more than a hundred people flocked to a meeting at the City of London Tavern. Here, according to Marc's journal, William Smith took the chair, resolutions were proposed and agreed upon, a committee was instituted and a list of subscriptions for shares was opened. Within days the committee began preparing the parliamentary Bill, which would create the Thames Tunnel Company and grant it permission to dig the tunnel.

Meanwhile, Marc attended to other strategic matters. On 5th March he explained his plan to the Duke of Wellington. 'His Grace,' he wrote later, 'made many very good observations and raised great objections; but after having explained to him my Plan and the expedients I had in reserve, His Grace appeared to be satisfied and to be disposed to subscribe.' Marc was fortunate in being not only a brilliant engineer but also a skilled lobbyist who recognised the inestimable value of good 'public relations' long before such a phrase was coined. The support of the Iron Duke was to be critical in the difficult years to come.

The Bill received the Royal Assent on 24th June 1824 and at the Company's first general meeting in their new City offices the terms of Marc's appointment were described: as Engineer to the Company he was given a salary of £1,000 a year; in addition he was to have £5,000 for the use of his patent, to be paid 'when the body of the tunnel shall be securely affected, and carried sixty feet beyond each embankment of the river' and a further and final sum of £5,000 'when the first public toll ... shall have been received...'

PREPARATIONS FOR DIGGING

One of the most important preparations before work could begin was the survey of the earth under the river bed: time-consuming test borings along the proposed course of the tunnel at an early stage could prevent a disaster later on. The samples showed Marc

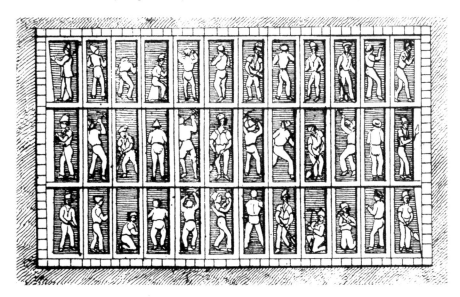

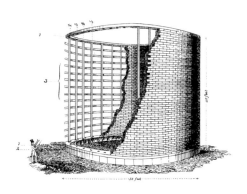

that upwards from 42 ft there was loose, water-bearing gravel; below 76 ft he risked meeting the quicksand which had sunk Trevithick's tunnel. Marc therefore decided to send the tunnel along at a depth and gradient where the samples told him he would find strong blue clay. This would be an easy material to tunnel through, but would also hold up well. Nevertheless, if it were only 34 ft thick it made the importance of the excavation staying on course even greater. It also meant that, at the river's deepest point, the 'crown' of the tunnel arch would be only 14 ft below the bed of the Thames.

On 2nd March 1825 the work began.

SINKING THE TUNNEL SHAFT

Like Vazie before him, Marc's first requirement was a shaft on the Rotherhithe side of the river to provide access to the place where the tunnel would start. The traditional method was to dig a shaft and line the walls with bricks. This meant holding up the digging while underpinnings were driven into the sides of the shaft in order to keep the lining in place. But Marc's ingenious idea was to build a brick tower and then simply allow it to sink it into the soft river-bank through the downward force of its own weight, thereby saving both time and money.

William Smith, M.P., now Chairman of the Thames Tunnel Company, performed the opening ceremony, Marc laid the first brick and his son Isambard laid the second.

Afterwards, the important guests sat down to lunch and to listen to earnest and optimistic speeches about the tunnel, to admire the model of it made for the occasion out of icing sugar and to drink a toast to its success. Twelve bottles of Bordeaux were purposely put aside to be drunk at the celebration on the far side of the river on a day, it was then thought, about three years in the future.

In three weeks, the circular shaft – or tower as it appeared at first – had been built: its strong wall consisted of an inner and an outer surface of bricks a yard apart, the cavity between them filled with cement and rubble. It was 42 ft high and 50 ft across, built on top of a 25-ton iron hoop and was strengthened with another hoop at the top, the two of them tied by iron rods running vertically between the shaft's two brick walls. A superstructure was then set on top of the tower on which a steam-engine was assembled to pump away the water which the shaft encountered as it sank and to bring up buckets of earth from the bottom.

Thus, the excavation began and the enormous construction, weighing nearly 1,000 tons, was carefully sunk into the ground under its own weight at the rate of a few

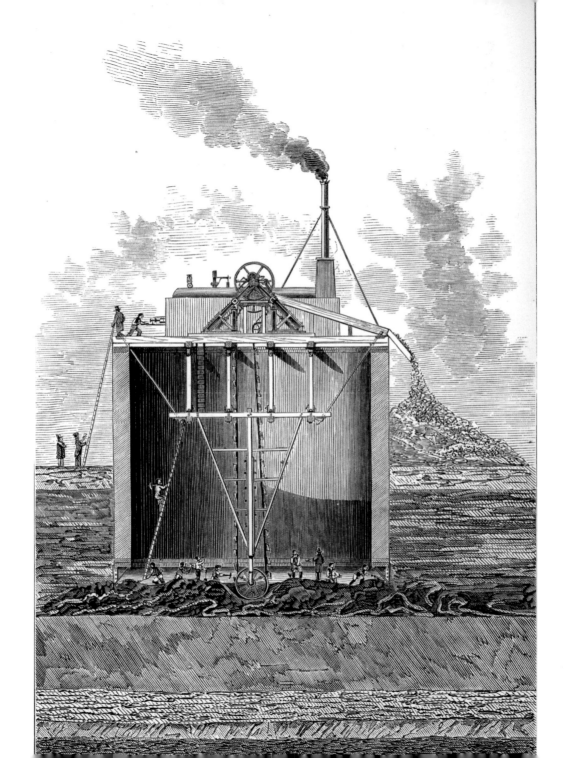

A watercolour by George Yates. Marc produced a bas-relief design of the tunnelling shield on a neighbouring building. Isambard arranged for the shaft to be enclosed to protect the engine. The first casualty was a drunken worker who fell down the well, which was soon closed

inches a day. Very soon, the downwards progress of the shaft at Rotherhithe became one of the most popular and fashionable sights of London. The Duke of Wellington was among the first to inspect it.

On 3rd June 1825, the shaft had just two feet more to sink but would go no further under its own weight. So Marc ordered another 8,000 bricks to be added to the top rim. When this failed to have an effect, he ordered more... and more ... until 50,000 had been added. With still no movement, he ordered the steam pumping engine to be turned off. The cylinder began to fill with water from underground springs, softening the earth and slowly the shaft began its downward journey again.

By 6th June 1825 the top of the brick tower was below ground level. The shaft was not yet complete, however: it had to be given a foundation. The diggers continued downward below the bottom of the pre-fabricated brickwork for another 20 ft or so, and bricklayers were employed again to finish the walls, leaving an opening 36 ft wide facing north for the tunnelling shield.

At the very bottom of the shaft a reservoir was dug and covered, which would hold the water drained from the tunnel workings. Above the shaft Marc installed a new, more powerful steam-engine of his own design, with a boiler house beside it, to drive the tunnel pumps and bring up the earth in buckets. Finally, the great shield, built for Marc by Henry Maudslay, was lowered into place 63 ft below the ground and on about 25th November 1825 the boring of the tunnel began.

THE SHIELD

The shield that was assembled at the bottom of the Rotherhithe shaft in November differed considerably in its details from the earlier ones Marc had designed. It was composed, finally, of twelve frames. Each was 3 ft wide, 21 ft high and 6 ft deep from front to back and contained three miners' cells. When it was fully manned, as it was by two eight-hour shifts, thirty-six miners would be excavating a tunnel face of approximately 800 sq ft.

A sectional drawing showing the fast-setting Roman cement being lifted up to the work stage

At the foot of each frame, to spread its weight of more than seven tons and prevent it from sinking, there stood a large 'shoe'. The joint between the frame and its shoe allowed the frame to pivot and so lean forwards or backwards if necessary.

Above the head of each frame were rollers carrying staves which supported the unlined portion of the tunnel's ceiling, while the face of the tunnel was supported by the small, removable 'poling boards'.

The 'hydraulic jacks' Marc had originally envisaged were replaced by 'screw jacks'. Working on the same principle as a modern car jack, these moved the frames of the shield forward into the lengthening tunnel by thrusting backwards onto the ends of the tunnel's brick lining. This was to be at least 2 ft 6 in. thick in every part and was to be built with a new kind of 'Roman' cement, whose strength Marc had tested exhaustively and the expense of which he vigorously defended.

ISAMBARD ON BOARD

It was not long before misfortune struck. Marc had been taken ill even before the tunnelling got under way. Then, in August 1826, his resident engineer, John Armstrong, also became ill through overwork and resigned. The work was then run by Richard Beamish, an ex-Guardsman; William Gravatt, a mathematician; and Isambard. The young Brunel often stayed below ground supervising the progress of the great shield for thirty six hours at a stretch. In fact, late in 1825, his over-exertion had made him ill, but in the busy months that followed Isambard proved his flair and durability to the satisfaction of the directors of the Thames Tunnel Company, and on 3rd January 1827 his appointment as resident engineer was made official. Thus it was that the resident engineer to a project on which was focused the attention of the nation, of Europe and of much of the western world, was a young man of twenty.

For fear of further damage to his health and therefore to the progress of the tunnel, Isambard was given three assistants: Beamish, Gravatt, and Francis Riley. But almost immediately Riley caught river fever from the foul water in the tunnel, became delirious and died. Later, Beamish, too, fell seriously ill more than once and was left blind in one eye. It is important to remember that at this time, long before the comprehensive sewer system built by Joseph Bazalgette, the River Thames was the recipient of all the sewage and industrial effluent of the metropolis and the riverbed was a stinking, highly toxic substance.

Isambard Kingdom Brunel

OPPOSITE
Watercolour by Frederick Goodall, showing the cross arches and railway trucks, one of six paintings commissioned by the Brunels

RAISING AND SAVING MONEY

As if their own illnesses and that of assistants, workmen and overseers were not enough for the Brunels to worry about, in February 1827, with 300 ft of the archway completed, the directors of the tunnel decided to allow the general public to admire the work.

Marc protested. The promised seam of 'strong blue clay' proved to be far from continuous, giving way in many places to gravel, and so he was in constant fear of a disaster. The very real possibility that the river might burst in when there were dozens of sightseers present horrified him. But his protests were in vain and at the end of April up to seven hundred visitors were being admitted daily, each paying one shilling.

The directors also proposed to save money by cutting the workmen's wages. This resulted in a strike and in the words of *The Times* of 1st May, 'scenes of riot and confusion' followed. It ended after three days, but the strike leaders were not re-employed.

THE FIRST FLOOD

In mid-May the increasing amount of water in the tunnel became a major cause of concern. Pieces of china, wood, coal and other debris were being found by the miners as they worked in the upper frames of the shield, indicating that the bottom of the river was very close. On 18th May, after showing yet another party of – apparently aristocratic – visitors along the tunnel, Marc wrote: 'I attended Lady Raffles to the frames, most uneasy all the while as if I had a presentiment...' His fears proved justified. That evening, as the tide was rising, water suddenly came roaring through one of the shield's frames. In the course of making their escape, Richard Beamish and Isambard paused at the visitors' barrier for a last look before ascending the shaft. A torrent of water was rushing towards them – they reached the top of the stairs just in time.

The accident cost no lives and Marc actually confessed himself relieved now that what he had long feared had finally occurred. Two days later he was evidently in a confident mood, writing in his journal: 'The Rotherhithe curate, in his sermon today, adverting to the accident, said that it was but a just judgement on the presumptuous aspirations of mortal men, etc... The poor man!'

However, all work was suspended and Isambard went down to the riverbed in a diving-bell borrowed from the East India Docks Company. There he found the cause of

the inundation: gravel dredgers had been at work and the top of the shield had indeed been too close to the river bottom. But the brickwork remained sound and repairs were promptly organised. A bed of iron rods was laid across the gap between the brickwork and the head of the shield, and bags of clay placed on top. In little more than three weeks sufficient clay had been laid to seal the hole and allow the pumping of water from the tunnel to begin.

The project continued to attract public interest. Isambard's venture in the diving-bell was accompanied by boatloads of sightseers and reporters. And even while repairs were still in progress Isambard and his assistants were obliged by the directors to show visitors along the partly cleared tunnel in a punt. During one such visit the punt capsized and a miner was drowned – the second death to occur in the tunnel's construction but, unfortunately, not the last.

In August 1827, Marc suffered a paralytic stroke brought on by the pressures of the project. In September Richard Beamish caught pleurisy, which kept him off work for six weeks. The workmen too suffered – the flooding of the tunnel had damaged the ventilation, so that as well as foul water, the men also had to contend with foul air, which left a deposit of black grime around their nostrils.

ABOVE
The diving bell, by Clarkson Stanfield

RIGHT
Sketch, probably Marc, showing the effect of the first flood and Isambard inspecting the damage

OPPOSITE
Sketch by Isambard showing how he used the diving bell after the first inundation

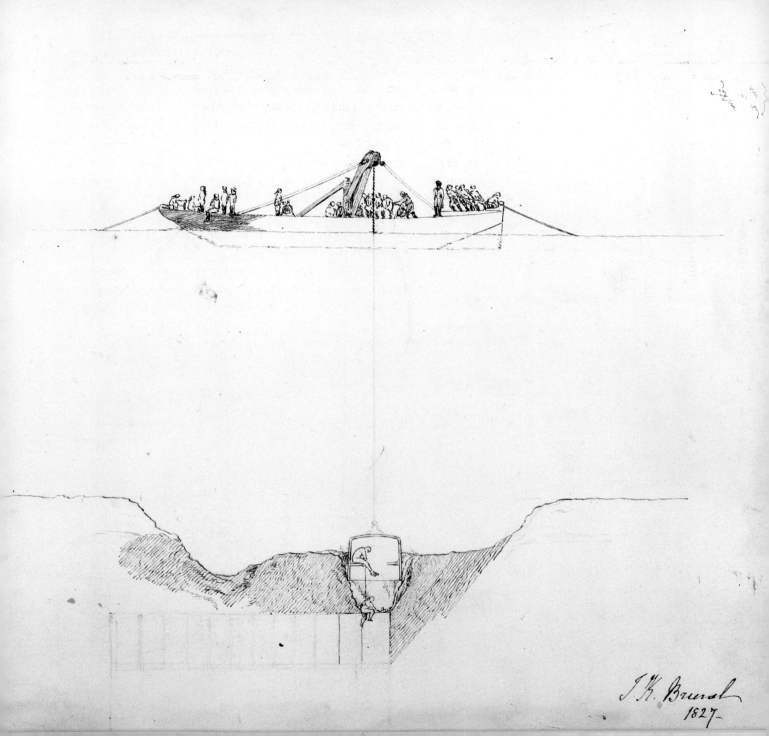

I.K. Brunel
1827

THE BANQUET UNDER THE RIVER

By November 1827, the tunnel had been cleared of water and silt and the shield was ready to begin work once again. Although Marc was still far from completely fit, Isambard set about organising a celebratory banquet, largely to restore confidence among the directors of the company, the workforce and the public. And the banquet would take place in the tunnel itself, on 10th November, in case any were still in doubt about the state of things underground.

In the western archway, draped in crimson, a long table was covered in white damask and elaborately set with silver and crystal for a sumptuous banquet. Fifty selected guests, lit by decorative candelabra from the Portable Gas Company, dined while the uniformed band of the Coldstream guards played the National Anthem, *Rule Britannia* and *See the Conquering Hero Comes*. Their instruments gleaming only faintly in the darkness of the tunnel, the noise they produced in this confined space was deafening. It was a hoarse set of guests who toasted 'The King', 'The Duke of Clarence' and 'The Duke of Wellington'.

In the eastern archway, 120 miners and bricklayers enjoyed a simpler meal, toasted their tools, and presented Isambard with pickaxe and shovel as token of their esteem, and added a toast of their own: 'To our tools ! '.

One of the guests was an artist, probably George Jones, and he later captured the scene in an oil painting. Two figures confer in the foreground – they are Marc and Isambard. This is the only painting of father and son together, but is even more remarkable because Marc was not well enough to attend the banquet!

WORSE TO COME

However, from the moment the work restarted, the quality of the earth being excavated once more gave cause for concern and, on the morning of 12th January 1828, disaster struck again, worse than before.

A shift was about to end. Isambard was working in the shield, helping two miners called Collins and Ball to remove some shoring in one of the frames. Suddenly a torrent of water swept in, knocked them out of the frame and extinguished all the lights. A fallen timber trapped Isambard's leg but he managed to free himself. The tunnel was rapidly filling with water and Isambard struggled to the bottom of the shaft, calling in the darkness to the miners to do likewise. By the time he reached the foot of the shaft the workmen's stairs were blocked by others trying to get out, so he turned and made for the visitors' staircase. At this point he was swept up by an immense wave which came sweeping along the tunnel. On reaching the shaft it was forced upwards, actually reaching the very top of the 42-ft Rotherhithe shaft. As it did so, it bore Isambard's battered body up to safety.

DEATH AND INJURY

In fifteen minutes the length of the 600-ft tunnel was under water. A press report recounted: 'Wives and children in a state of nudity, the accident happening at such an early hour, were seen in the utmost state of distress, eagerly enquiring after their husbands and fathers.'

Six men died, including Collins and Ball, who, unlike Isambard, had not recovered from the initial irruption of water at the shield. They were found later, crushed under the great wooden stage located behind the shield, upon which the bricklayers stood to

Water rushes through one of the frames, 12th January 1828

construct the tunnel arch. Four others had reached the shaft and were trying to ascend it by ladder, only to be sucked from it by the force of the great wave as it recoiled.

Isambard refused to leave the works and immediately ordered the diving-bell again. Prevented from walking by the injury to his knee, he directed Gravatt's inspections of the damage while lying on a mattress on the diving-bell's barge. He was badly hurt. Not only had his leg been damaged but, it was later discovered, he had internal injuries so grave that he needed a long convalescence. This was made longer, he claimed, by 'returning too soon to a full diet' while recuperating in Brighton. The result was that on 8th February, to his great annoyance, he suffered the first of a series of haemorrhages and was (in his own words) 'laid up, quite useless' for more than three months. He was soon afterwards sent to sedate Clifton, where he would have fewer parties to attend and the odd bridge to design.

'FORTITUDE AND DETERMINATION'

Marc reacted stoically to the disaster. He immediately wrote to his company directors, expressing his certainty that the tunnel could be restored and completed. A reporter from *The New Times* wrote that '. . . far from giving way to that despondency, which some misdirected accounts have attributed to him, [he] appears to possess additional fortitude and determination'.

With Isambard laid up, Marc took to the diving-bell in all the violence of the river in January to explore the hole. The damage was much more severe than the last time: in the previous May 150 tons of clay had been sufficient to allow the pumps to make some headway in clearing the flooded tunnel; this time thirty times that amount had to be dumped on the riverbed before the work could proceed.

And when darkness brought an end to the day's work at the waterside, Marc was frequently obliged by the company directors to spend his evenings ploughing through the hundreds of hare-brained schemes for repairing or completing the tunnel from well-meaning members of the public. He also had other work to think about: a floating pier at Blackwall and plans for the Oxford Canal were also demanding his time.

On 21st January pumping began, although no sooner was some visible progress made than new holes appeared over the head of the shield. But by the end of March the dumping of clay was gradually producing the desired effect and the pumps were winning the battle against such water as was still seeping in. The shield could now be approached from inside the tunnel. In May the workmen were able to begin clearing silt,

An oil painting by Frederick Goodall: the body of a drowned miner is recovered

debris and flotsam from the archway and from the cells of the shield, and on 26th May, Whit Monday, a large number of visitors, keen as ever to inspect the work, were shown into the re-decorated western arch. The restoration of the shield could now begin.

FINANCIAL PROBLEMS

A fortnight after the disaster a meeting of the shareholders learned from the board of directors that there was only £21,000 left for the continuation of the work. Marc reiterated his complete confidence in overcoming future problems underground, provided there were adequate funds to do so. The first 'irruption' had not ended the tunnel's progress – it had since been extended another 52 ft to within 25 ft of the middle of the river – so why should this one? The meeting was subdued, but it closed without blame being placed on Marc, and at the end he departed to revise the estimates for the tunnel's restoration and completion.

At a second meeting on 4th March an engineer called Francis Giles put forward a proposal to take over from Marc and complete the tunnel as a single thoroughfare for pedestrians only. Giles had made an earlier bid to oust Marc after the first disaster, which had found favour for a while, particularly with the chairman, William Smith.

A publicity drawing amended to show the position of the second inundation

This time the subscribers rallied immediately to the support of the inventor of the shield: whereas Marc's tunnel would be the 'pride of the Empire', the modified proposal would reduce it to 'a mere gimlet hole and a disgrace'.

Yet the problem of finance remained. A bill enabling the company to raise a further £250,000 in two stages received the Royal Assent in May 1828, and a committee of the company directors set about publicising and promoting a further issue of shares to existing shareholders to ensure, as far as possible, that this would receive a favourable reception and raise the full amount of money needed to complete the tunnel.

SUPPORT FROM THE IRON DUKE

Not for the first time in Marc's career, the Duke of Wellington now stepped forward to declare publicly his confidence in the great engineer. At the public launch of the renewed call for investment he spoke at considerable length. There was no work, he said, upon which the public interest of foreign nations had been more excited. Men could not help seeing the benefit to the immediate neighbourhood and the neighbouring counties, let alone the great political, military and commercial profit that would be derived from the example of such a work.

After defending Marc for overstepping his original estimate of the costs of the work, the Duke stated that altogether another £200,000 was needed and that if it were raised nothing would stop the tunnel being completed. The accidents, he said to applause, had only served to demonstrate the enterprise, genius and ability of the engineer who had conducted the undertaking and that the work itself was excellent. With a final appeal to their patriotic spirit, he assured the audience that, once completed, the tunnel would be 'durable in proportion as the honour of having completed it will be durable to this country' and he earnestly entreated their assistance to carry on 'this great work'. Those present, including the Duke himself, hurried to subscribe.

Yet the optimism was short-lived. The country had not yet recovered from the economic slump following the end of years of war with France. Although the project still excited the interest of the general public, not even the promise of the eventual profits held out by the Iron Duke could exhort them to put their money into it. Three weeks after his call for investment the subscriptions totalled £9,600, less than a twentieth of the money needed.

THE TUNNEL BRICKED UP

With no more money, there was no way to finish the tunnel, so it was bricked up (with the shield inside); Gravatt, Beamish, the miners and the bricklayers were paid off. Marc's diary for 9th August 1828 contains the sad entry: 'Saw the last of the frames!!!'

'The tunnel is now blocked up at the end...' wrote Isambard. 'A year ago I should have thought this intolerable ... now it is come – like all other events – only at a distance do they appear to be dreaded.'

A large mirror was mounted on the new wall, giving the illusion to the sightseers who would continue to be admitted of the continuous archway which the Brunels still hoped one day to see completed.

At the end of October Marc and Sophia set off for France, leaving Isambard with the none-too-onerous task of maintaining the tunnel. On his return, Marc had more meetings with the directors, but derived greater pleasure from going back to his drawing-board, taking time to exclaim in his diary: 'Engaged on shield!'

The tunnel meanwhile became, at home at any rate, the object of considerable scoffing. *The Times* had taken to calling it 'the Great Bore', and the poet Thomas Hood, in his *Ode to Monsieur Brunel*, advised the engineer to turn the tunnel into a wine cellar.

WELL! Monsieur Brunel,
How prospers now thy mighty undertaking,
To join by a hollow way the Bankside friends
Of Rotherhithe, and Wapping,
Never be stopping,
But poking, groping, in the dark keep making
An archway, underneath the Dabs and Gudgeons,
For Collier men and pitchy old Curmudgeons,
To cross the water in inverse proportion,
Walk under steam-boats under the keel's ridge.
To keep down all extortion,
And without sculls to diddle London Bridge!
In a fresh hunt, a new Great Bore to worry,
Thou didst to earth thy human terriers follow;
Hopeful at last from Middlesex to Surrey,
To give us the "View hollow."
In short it was thy aim, right north and south,
To put a pipe into old Thames's mouth;
Alas! half-way thou hadst proceeded, when
Old Thames, through roof, not water-proof,
Came, like "a tide in the affairs of men;"
And with a mighty stormy kind of roar,
Reproachful of thy wrong,
Burst out in that old song
Of Incledon's*, beginning "Cease, rude Bore"

Sad is it, worthy of one's tears,
Just when one seems the most successful,
To find one's self o'er head and ears
In difficulties most distressful!
Other great speculations have been nursed,
Till want of proceeds laid them on a shelf;
But thy concern was at the worst,
When it began to liquidate itself!
But now Dame Fortune has her false face hidden,
And languishes thy Tunnel, – so to paint,
Under a slow incurable complaint,
Bed-ridden!
Why, when thus Thames – bed-bother'd –
why repine!
Do try a spare bed at the Serpentine!
Yet let none think thee daz'd, or craz'd, or stupid;
And sunk beneath thy own and Thames's craft;
Let them not style thee some Mechanic Cupid
Pining and pouting o'er a broken shaft!
I'll tell thee with thy tunnel what to do;
Light up thy boxes, build a bin or two,
The wine does better than such water trades:
Stick up a sign – the sign of the Bore's Head;
I've drawn it ready for thee in black lead,
And make thy cellar subterrane, Thy Shades?

* Charles Benjamin Incledon (1763–1826) was the finest
tenor of his day, and became particularly famous for his
delivery of stirring ballads.

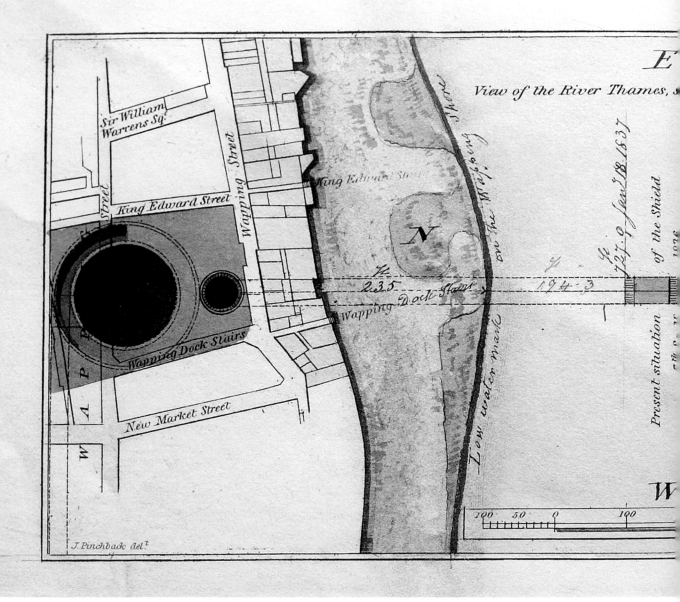

View of the River Thames, s

E

W

Sir William Warrens Sq.

Wapping Street

King Edward Street

King Edward Street

N

Wapping Dock Stairs

Wapping Dock Stairs

New Market Street

Low water mark

on the Wapping Shore

2.3.5

19 ft. 3

727.0 Jan.th 18. 1637

Present situation

of the Shield

100   50   0   100

J. Pinchback del.t

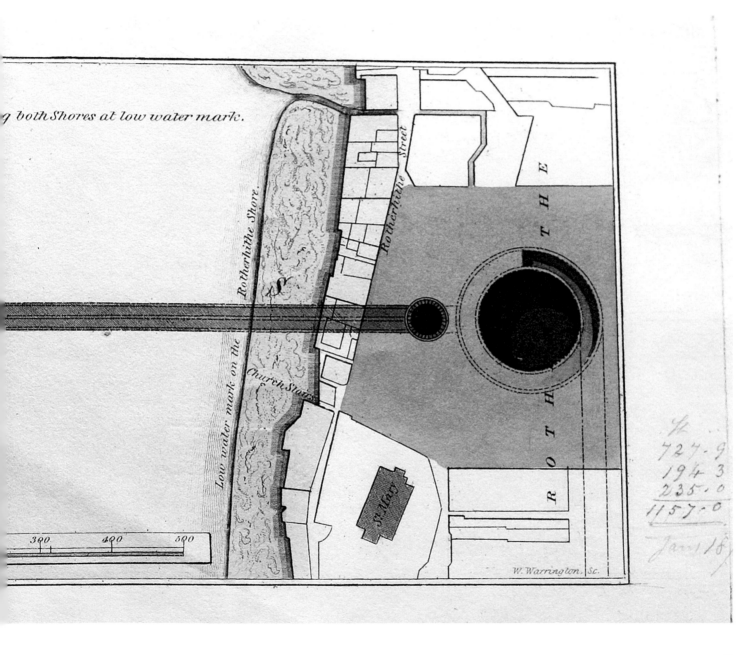

g both Shores at low water mark.

Rotherhithe Shore.

Rotherhithe Street

Low water mark on the

Church Stairs

T H E

R O T H

ST MARY

W. Warrington. Sc.

300   400   500

½
727·9
194 3
235·0
1157·0

Jan 18

Finishing the Tunnel

THE ATTEMPT TO OUST MARC

All tunnelling had stopped, yet from January 1829 onwards, Marc continued to work on improvements to the design of the shield, lobbying support for restarting the tunnel and petitioning the government for the finance which was not forthcoming from the public. Much of his energy was spent trying to overcome the obstructions of William Smith. The chairman of the directors took the view that, with Marc in charge, the government would never lend any more money; indeed Smith seemed determined to prevent it doing so. Doing his best to sever Marc from any further involvement, he advanced the plans of another engineer. Fortunately, the shareholders were wary of Smith and on the basis of independent professional advice they rejected his proposal and voted that only Marc's plan be considered.

When the shareholders instructed the directors to apply for a government loan they were in for a shock. It emerged that the company had already been offered a loan of £250,000 but had declined it. This was Smith's doing and, worse, he had concealed it from the rest of the company. Marc patiently undid the damage and had a further clause added to a forthcoming Bill, effectively allowing the Tunnel Company to draw on the Exchequer Loan Commission fund. The Bill received the Royal Assent in September 1830.

At their next meeting the shareholders, wise to Smith's stratagems, prevented him from taking the chair and instructed the directors to ask the Exchequer for a loan.

At the end of November 1831, Marc suffered a heart attack but this was not the last misfortune of the year: on 20th December the application for a loan was rejected. Negotiations continued, but to Isambard, at least, they were merely the tunnel's death throes. 'Tunnel is now, I think, dead...', he wrote; 'It will never be finished now in my father's lifetime I fear...'.

But Marc did not share his son's pessimism and as 1832 came in he turned his thoughts to the Thames Tunnel Company's forthcoming Annual General Meeting. If

Smith continued as chairman it would be doubtful whether he could ever complete the tunnel, but the meeting in March offered a chance to remove him. Marc paved the way by sending to all the shareholders a letter that described in full Smith's furtive attempts to block a government loan.

It was a decisive meeting. Smith, to the general relief, was voted out. G. H. Wollaston, an old friend of Marc's, became chairman and Benjamin Hawes, the engineer's son-in-law, was made deputy chairman. Now at last Marc could count on strong and sympathetic support in the toils which undoubtedly remained.

MEANWHILE ...

Even when he was not occupied with the future of the tunnel, it was not in Marc's nature to sit idle. He revisited France, looking up old friends of his and Sophia's; he travelled extensively round England, visiting and admiring the work of other engineers and architects in cathedrals, docks and canals; and he undertook projects, including a bridge across the river Lea in Cork; he conducted experiments on the doomed 'Gaz' engine project and with a new type of bridge arch and with ship construction. His journal continually shows the keen interest with which he followed the progress of his fellow inventors: Lord Cochrane and his patent for tunnelling using pressure, and Babbage's calculating machine, an early form of computer ('truly admirable', wrote Marc). He gratefully accepted the honours which, even without the achievement that would crown his life's work, were heaped on him in recognition of all that he had done so far. To his own country's highest civil distinction, the Legion d'Honneur, and awards from Caen, Rouen and Stockholm, was added election, in November that year, to the Council of the Royal Society, the oldest and most important scientific society in Britain.

Isambard also occupied his time fully, undertaking scientific experiments with Charles Babbage and Michael Faraday. In 1829 he had taken himself off to Bristol, which led not only to his design for the Clifton Suspension Bridge, but also to his work on the Bristol docks, and thereby to the launch of his stellar career, independent of his father's.

It was the tunnel, however, that remained Marc's preoccupation. In May 1833 he even had an audience with King William IV, where they conversed in French. The engineer moved his office to Parliament Street in Westminster. Here he would be closer to the seat of government, as he knew that obtaining the government loan was the key to restarting the work.

REJECTION FOLLOWS REJECTION

Petitioning for a loan had not been a straightforward procedure up to now, and even after the removal of the obstructive William Smith there were still to be a series of setbacks. The last petition had been approved by Parliament on 15th February 1833, but, with insufficient funds at their disposal, the Loan Commissioners rejected it.

The Annual General Meeting of March 1834 voted to press another petition for a loan, but this time, on 18th March, Parliament rejected it. The company made arrangements to present it again at the next available Parliamentary opportunity but it was scuppered this time by an unanticipated misfortune:

April 29th: The tunnel petition was to have been presented this day by Major Beauclerk, but how it happened I know not, the petition was mislaid, and all our hopes frustrated again notwithstanding the assurances we have from every quarter of support.

Marc's restraint in describing the waste of such an opportunity speak volumes about his nature. But he may have been still buoyant following a party held four days earlier by a group of Fellows of the Royal Society in the upstairs room of the 'Spreadeagle & Crown' just across the road (now renamed 'The Mayflower' in commemoration of the departure of that ship from Rotherhithe for Virginia, with a local captain, in 1620). The Fellows vowed to meet each year to toast his health and so launched the Tunnel Club, which came to enjoy the reputation of a powerful pressure group and lobbying force.

The battle was indeed almost won. In mid-June Beauclerk at last presented the petition and the House approved it. While waiting to hear of the decision from the Treasury, Marc and Sophia went off on their travels again. They returned in mid-November and he again set about improving the design of the shield. At last, on 5th December, the Treasury made over £30,000 to the Thames Tunnel Company – the first instalment of the long-awaited loan.

PLANS FOR RESTARTING

As the workface in the tunnel would soon be closer to Wapping than Rotherhithe, Marc planned to ease its progress by transferring some of the services to that side from the southern shore: the supply of air to the tunnel would be fresher and drainage of water seeping into the workings would be carried out more effectively from the nearer side.

Marc also proposed that the company buy its own diving-bell – until now it had borrowed one as needed – with which he would survey the riverbed ahead of the tunnel. Clay and gravel would be dumped wherever the riverbed showed signs of a depression, preventing the disastrous irruptions of the kind that had occurred before whenever unforeseen valleys in the river bottom brought it too close to the head of the shield.

The new shield, too, would be an improvement: closer to the idea in Marc's original patent, with extended staves at the top and sides to overlap with the tunnel brickwork and support the unbricked section of the roof when a frame was moved forward.

Sadly, except for the improvements to the shield, all the proposals came to nothing. The obstacle lay in the Treasury's conditions for its £270,000 loan: the terms stated that the money was to be 'solely applied for carrying on the tunnel itself' and that 'no advance should be applied to defray any other expenses until that part of the undertaking which is most hazardous shall be secured'.

Although Marc and the directors of the company tried long and hard, they could not persuade the Loan Commissioners to see the wisdom of his plans. The only concessions were for building an improved shield (there was no question of using the old one in any case, as it had been bricked up and rusting for the past seven years) and buying a vessel, the *Ganges*, from which to drop the clay filling onto the riverbed. The firm of Henry Maudslay, maker of the original shield, was asked to quote for the new one, but in the event the price offered by the Rennie Brothers' firm was lower.

Marc and Sophia moved to a house in Cow Court, Rotherhithe, opposite the works. Meanwhile, Isambard's fortunes continued to improve. By now he was too busy ushering the Great Western Railway Bill through Parliament and surveying route of this line to resume his post of engineer-in-charge. So it was to Richard Beamish, his former assistant, that the position went in January 1835.

RE-OPENING

In the tunnel, there was much to do: rotten timbers in stairways, stages, waste-trucks and hoist had to be replaced; ropes, too, had rotted; the steam-engine and pumps had to be overhauled, the brick wall had to be demolished, and so on. Dismantling and

A vision of the tunnel *c.*1830

removing the old shield got under way at the end of August, yet such was the strain of the work in this oxygen-starved environment that in October Beamish and two of his three assistants fell ill.

Nevertheless, by the end of the year Marc was pleased with the achievements. 'We have done wonders,' he wrote in his diary, 'in having accomplished so much without any accident. . . may we be as fortunately circumstanced at the end of the year 1836. Thanks be to God!'

Such was the complexity and the weight of the new shield – it was more than 50 tons heavier than the old one – that the new year was almost three months old before it was assembled. But tunnelling got underway quickly and a month later 15 ft of new tunnel had been built; by the end of April the rate of progress was 4 ft 6 in. a week.

But before long there were problems at all levels of the workforce. The bricklayers were often in the local pubs, too drunk to report for their shift and the rate of advance fell back to 2 ft 6 in. a week. In August Beamish, having failed to get the sixty per cent pay rise he had asked for, offered his resignation. Then Marc heard that two of Beamish's assistants, Page and Gordon, would refuse to serve under anyone else. So Page was appointed Acting Engineer, but Gordon, despite a salary increase, left.

It then came to light that the assistants were not using the shield in the correct way. This caused parts to fracture and break, which, in turn, made some frames drop below their proper level, hindering the tunnel's ascent. Following this there were problems with the drainage. Nonetheless, Page proved a worthy resident engineer and by December 1836 progress since his appointment had risen again, to an average of four feet a week.

In the new year, however, this progress was not maintained: miners, foremen and assistant engineers alike fell sick, thanks to the influx of water. By February it was coming in at a rate of 230 gallons a minute, whereas 100 gallons a minute was the usual average figure, and to pump it away was a major problem. When the water was not full of silt, which jammed the legs of the frames and damaged the pumps, it bore even more gas, which caused frequent vomiting and occasional unconsciousness.

Professor Taylor of Guy's Hospital was to some extent already familiar with the symptoms that the water caused, because throughout the history of the digging it was to Guy's Hospital in east London that the men had gone for treatment. He now analysed a sample and found it to be contaminated with two or three per cent sulphurated hydrogen gas. In time, he wrote, breathing this would cause 'nausea, loss of appetite, great feebleness, tremor of the limbs and general wasting of the body'. And, as if to reinforce Marc's argument before tunnelling restarted, Taylor's report went on: 'The most effectual means of purifying the air would be . . . a communication with the northern shore so that there might be a continual current through the tunnel.'

'VOMITING FLAMES OF FIRE'

From June Marc's journal carries frequent reports of an alarming and highly dangerous phenomenon, which was familiar in collieries but which had not been reported in the tunnel before: gas explosions, known to coal miners as 'fire damp'.

> *June 17th. The gas, collected under the tails of number 8* [frame], *exploded on the approach of a light.*
> *June 28th. The gas ... ignites frequently, that is at every tide – sometimes with violence. One man was burnt – singed.*
> *July 4th. The explosions have been more violent than before and the ignition excessively heating – work could not proceed.*

The type of ignition varied. Sometimes there was a sudden sharp explosion, at other times a continual fire, which on one occasion burned for three and three quarter hours. A report from Thomas Page describes it vividly:

> *July 14th. While number 2* [frame] *was blowing out torrents of water, number 12 was vomiting flames of fire, which burned with a roaring noise – in less than three minutes it melted the side of a pint pot partly filled with water.*

The solution lay in better ventilation, but the Treasury was not persuaded to help with the remedy. Marc, persistent as ever, proposed to sink the shaft on the Wapping side, put a second shield in place and start tunnelling southwards. He argued in detail the savings that would be made if the miners could work at one face when conditions prevented them from working at the other. The directors supported his case and presented it to the Treasury. In mid-July, after an alarming influx of water and gravel from one of the frames, Marc took the precaution of having a second ramp built behind the shield in the eastern arch so that if a major flood occurred, the workmen could remain above water and escape in the direction of the Rotherhithe shaft. The eventual response from the Treasury may have not been a surprise: 'Their Lordships... cannot give their authority to proceeding in any other manner with the

Reconstruction of the gas explosions by Windfall Films

work than that which has already been sanctioned...' The shaft at Wapping would have to wait.

PAGE PREVENTS DISASTER

In the early morning of 23rd August there was concern at the level of the water in the Tunnel. At 4 a.m. Marc had come down to keep an eye on the situation but at 9 a.m. had returned home. At midday Thomas Page asked for a last report before leaving the shaft to go to a directors' meeting. The assistant engineer told him that water was coming in rapidly through frames 11 and 12, and Page, abandoning his meeting, went down to the shield himself. So far the other frames remained dry, but he ordered them to be blocked up all the same and sent Brunel a note expressing his fear that the high tide that afternoon would bring a flood. Then he gave orders that the tunnel should be closed to visitors and that a raft should be prepared at the bottom of the shaft to ferry bricks and clay to the shield when the railway used to remove the excavated material became submerged. Returning to the shield he found the inflow had all but stopped, but within a few minutes it 'burst out again with increased violence, and continued running again without any diminution'. By the afternoon more materials were needed to block the frames than the raft could carry, so Page ordered the boat from the *Ganges* to be brought down and used.

All afternoon, the water greatly outstripped the pumps and, as one shift relieved another, Page instructed the men to continue blocking up the frames. When he was satisfied that the men had done all they could to confine the breach to numbers 11 and 12 he ordered them to go up and he and his two foremen followed along the recently built ramp.

Page tried to make a further inspection of the shield by boat, but at his second attempt the water was surging in and it was time to make for the staircase in the shaft. By 5.30 p.m. the gas lamps near the shield were submerged, but the men lingered in fascination around the bottom of the staircase until Page again ordered them upstairs. 'Eventually,' he wrote later, 'when the water had risen to within fifty feet of the entrance of the tunnel, it came forward in a wave, and Mr Francis and Mr Mason, Williams and Fitzgerald and I who were at the bottom of the visitors' stairs, ran up to the second landing whence we saw it fill the bottom of the shaft, and from there [we] came up to the top.'

At an early stage in the disaster Page had realised the situation was serious, but his capable management of the men meant they kept working without panicking and so prevented the flood from being very much worse. His evacuation had been, as the following evening's edition of the *True Sun* noted, orderly and without loss of life.

That evening, accompanied by Isambard, Marc took to the river aboard the *Ganges*, and as soon as they had found where the clay was needed the repair work began. As usual, the engineer was cheerful. Asked if he had expected this flood, he replied: 'Why yes. I have been honoured with two visitations of Father Thames during the first half of the work and I cannot hope to escape without one at least in the other'.

The workings were restored at speed: in three days the pumps were at work and eight days later they had finished. Then, six hundred 600 cubic yards of mud had to be removed. Tunnelling restarted on 11th September. But the gas continued to cause explosions or burned steadily, making the iron shield and the atmosphere exceedingly hot. When it was not burning, the gas was poisoning: there were more and more admissions to Guy's Hospital. Marc again pleaded to be allowed to sink the Wapping shaft, but to no avail. The Treasury's policy on the tunnel remained, as one newspaper wittily noted, 'one-sided'.

ANOTHER FLOOD

The appalling conditions at the face cost hundreds of lost man-hours weekly and progress was painfully slow. The tunnel had proceeded no more than 6½ft when the river came in again and in a much less controlled manner.

In the early hours of 3rd November, when Page was ill in bed, the assistant engineer, Francis, was on duty when a high tide brought a run of sand through one of

Heraldic emblem of a miner with a portrait of Marc from the *Illustrated London News*

the frames. This increased sharply and was soon followed by torrents of water. The alarm was raised and in about five minutes the tunnel was filling up. A few seconds after Francis and three other men had reached the top of the shaft the water arrived too, and with such force that it deposited a thick layer of mud in the street. Garland, a miner who had been asleep in one of the lower cells of the shield, was drowned, but at least seventy men had escaped and the tunnel, despite the force of the influx, was not damaged, to Marc's satisfaction, 'beyond a few bricks'. Once again, clay dumped over the head of the shield stopped the leak and in little more than a week the tunnel was clear.

Still the Treasury refused to allow any of the loan to be diverted to sinking the shaft at Wapping, so Marc arranged for a new shipping channel to be dredged south of the workface, closer to the Rotherhithe side, so that neither ships nor their anchors should disturb the riverbed over the shield. He also made changes to the poling. Originally designed to hold up a solid face, they were actually having to hold back liquid mud, so he fitted each with latches, which in effect meant that the boards formed a continuous, rigid barrier.

During the remaining two weeks of December the tunnel grew by ten feet, matching the total progress made in the first five months of the year. Even so, Marc calculated the average progress in 1837 to be just nine-tenths of an inch a day. But with the men aboard the *Ganges* dumping bags of clay over her side, the shield went steadily ahead. By 20th March the tunnel's length had reached 775 ft and the face was now less than 150 ft from the low-tide mark at Wapping. But there was more trouble to come.

'RUN! RUN!'

Richard Fletcher had been appointed assistant to Thomas Page in January 1838. On the morning of 20th March, as he finished his night shift, he was inspecting the upper faces of the shield when he noticed water seeping in through frames 11 and 12. Suddenly, with no more warning than a loud rumbling noise, a torrent of water gushed out from frame 11. 'Run! Run!' went the cry, and Fletcher, the bricklayers, labourers and the few miners present rushed up the western arch. Williams, the miners' foreman, followed and at the foot of the shaft he met a few other workers coming down to investigate the noise. Together they went to see if they could block up the leaking frame; but before they had got half way they found that it was hopeless: a wave of water and timber debris was bearing down on them fast. They turned back and fortunately all got up the stairs in time. In fifteen minutes the tunnel was full – for the third time in 26 ft of tunnelling. The breach in the riverbed was sealed in the usual way and ten days later the shield was reached. Inspecting the offending frame, Marc found that several of his new latch bolts were fractured – this must have been the reason that the water had come in.

Just three weeks after the irruption all the mud had been cleared and tunnelling resumed: Marc went down to watch the work begin and the men on the shift gave him a cheer. 'Most gratifying indeed', he wrote.

Reconstruction of the flood by Windfall Films

'A GREATER NUMBER OF MEN DISABLED'

With the onset of warmer weather the effect of the gas in the tunnel began to be felt more acutely. Marc's diary for 1838 records one distressing instance after another:

May 4th. The effluvium was so offensive that some men were sick on the stage.
May 9th. Gas is particularly offensive… Mr Mason ill – he made his report to me of sickness, headache and weakness. Three assistants are ill …
May 16th. Much gas…the inflammable gas. Men complaining very much … Mason, who is returned, is in good spirits, but Francis is very bad.
May 17th. It appears that there is a greater number of disabled men than at any time before. I feel very much weakened by the inspection I made at the shield.

Marc Brunel by Samuel Drummond, *c.*1835 with a painting of the tunnel in the background

May 23rd. Minall is reported to be very ill. I gave directions accordingly for his successor.

May 24th. During the night Mr. Francis said that the gas burned fiercely and with a roaring like distant thunder.

May 26th. Heywood died this morning [of typhus]. Page is evidently sinking very fast ... It affects the eyes. I feel much debility after having been some time below. My sight is rather dim today. All complain of pain in the eyes. Dixon has reported that twice in one shift he was completely deprived of sight for some time.

May 28th. Wood, a bricklayer, fell senseless to the floor. The assistants complain of being affected in different ways.

May 29th. Short ... reported himself unable to work. Afflicted like Huggins and all the others ...

Bowyer died today or yesterday, a good man.

June 4th. Sullivan – sent him to hospital he being almost blind. Williams, the foreman of the first shift, gone. The men, the best men, are very much affected.

On 10th June a workman called Williams, whose behaviour had not been normal since the flood on 3rd November, had to be taken to a lunatic asylum 'as being too dangerous to be left out of doors'.

At the end of November Marc himself took to his bed for three weeks. It was not so much the conditions in the tunnel which affected him as the strain of getting up every two hours throughout the night to check the state of the works. When restored he applied yet again to the Treasury to be allowed to build the Wapping shaft. And yet again the Treasury remained adamant.

THE INGENIOUS MRS. BRUNEL

Sophia was seriously concerned by the toll the work was taking on her husband's health. Ever since the resumption of the work he had awoken every two hours to go to the tunnel office and check the latest report. In April 1839 Marc had celebrated his seventieth birthday and the constant working, day and night, would have taken its toll on even a young man's health. In June his wife made a modest but ingenious contribution to increasing her husband's nightly sleep: she organised a pulley, a cord, a bucket and a bell outside the bedroom window. When the bell rang and woke him, Marc pulled up the bucket on the end of the rope; he inspected the latest samples of earth and the night assistant's report, put any instructions of his own into the bucket, sent it down again and hoped to be asleep before it reached the ground.

TO WAPPING

The tunnel reached the low-water mark on the Wapping shore on 22nd August 1839. The men who had been employed to lay down bags of clay onto the riverbed were brought back into the tunnel and this, plus some improvements to the tunnel ventilation brought the rate of progress during October to nine feet a week. This was maintained through January and February 1840, despite exceptionally heavy rain which brought spring water into the tunnel. But on 3rd April, 500 gallons a minute were pouring in and the next morning an unlatched poling board gave way and 'with a sound like the roaring of thunder' an avalanche of gravel, slush and rocks came driving through the shield by the ton. With the lights out all around them the miners bravely stood their ground and managed to staunch the flow. This time, the damage could be seen above ground too: corresponding to the influx below, there was a hole in the Wapping foreshore, 13 ft deep and 30 ft across.

Despite this, on 11th June Marc took possession of the land for the Wapping shaft. Over the summer it was cleared, and in September the Rennies' firm delivered the iron curb – this shaft was to be sunk in the same way as the first.

THE MONEY PROBLEMS CONTINUE

The crises were not over yet, however. The government loan amounted to £270,000. Of this £190,000 had now been spent and Marc estimated that the shaft would cost £60,000. The directors panicked and demanded a flurry of sackings. Marc's loud protests secured a temporary compromise of sorts and the building of the shaft/tower began. In mid-November work on the tunnel stopped 45 ft short in case it disturbed the sinking of the shaft. 'I am truly happy to say that my arduous enterprise is drawing to a conclusion', Marc wrote. At the end of November Mason, assistant to Page, was dismissed and the directors told Page and Marc himself that they were unlikely to be paid after 25th March.

There were problems even with sinking the shaft: Rennie Bros. fell behind in building the steam-engine, which put the excavation for the shaft behind; in January the river iced over and, as the earth could not be removed by barge, all work came to a standstill.

But as the winter ended things improved: Marc, Page and Mason were re-employed and the Thames Tunnel Company's Annual General Meeting on 2nd March was buoyant with the prospect of both tunnel and shaft being completed soon and the prospect of revenue from foot passengers.

On 24th March 1840 Marc was publicly rewarded with the first official recognition of his achievement from his adopted country: a knighthood from Queen Victoria. He expressed his pleasure at the honour with restraint – in his journal at least:

24th. Levee of the Queen! Today Her Majesty was pleased to confer on me the honour of knighthood as Sir Isambart [sic] Brunel.

There was still work to do. In May a drainage and ventilation tunnel of small diameter was cut from a point under the main tunnel to beneath the new shaft. There was now a complete passage under the Thames and in June Marc's grandson, Isambard, aged three, was given the honour of becoming the first person to pass right under the river from shore to shore, followed by his father, his grandfather and the directors of the Thames Tunnel Company.

THE WAPPING SHAFT

The directors, in their continuing concern to save money, refused to purchase any more than the barest minimum of land on the northern shore. This meant, as Marc pointed out to them, that the shaft would be perilously close to a dense area of flimsily built and dilapidated buildings, many of them with little or no foundations. As so often throughout the troubled progress of this great enterprise, his judgment was proved right: as the shaft sank, subsidence took its toll and cracks appeared in the adjoining properties. The Thames Tunnel Company was then obliged to pay compensation to the owners for the damage.

As the Wapping shaft had now descended to meet the drainage tunnel, the shield could begin to move forward again without risk of damaging it. The tunnel progressed well in July, though the pumps were constantly draining water, flowing in at up to 450 gallons a minute. Shield and shaft were now within feet of each other and the downward pressure of the latter caused considerable damage to the shield to the extent that it had to be repaired to prevent a collapse.

At last came the day when Thomas Page came up from the tunnel on the Rotherhithe side and excitedly carried to the Brunels' house only yards away some

A view engraved long before the tunnel was complete but nevertheless reasonably accurate, by Tombleson & Co

red brick dust excavated at the shield: the tunnel had reached the shaft! It was 16th November 1841. Since the day when the digging of the tunnel had begun, sixteen years had passed and, as Marc wrote to his friend Charles Babbage, 'numberless difficulties of the most formidable character' had been overcome. To his friend James Howard he wrote that the enterprise:

has been one of inconceivable labours, difficulties and dangers...In fact, the four Elements were at one time particularly against us; Fire from the explosive gases, the same that are fatal in mines; Air... by the influence of which the men most exposed were sometimes removed quite senseless; Earth from the most terrific disruptions of the ground; Water from five irruptions of the river, three of which since the resumption of the work in 1836!

MAKING READY

The great shield's work was done. A few weeks later the frames were moved into the shaft and piece by piece they were hauled to the surface. Marc would have liked the shield to have formed the centre piece of an exhibition about the tunnel's construction, as he made clear in a letter to his directors:

Although in a merchantile point of view its [the shield's] value is no more than that of the old material, it will be gratifying to me and interesting to all those who seek information upon the construction of the tunnel, and were I in possession of it I should endeavour to make such arrangement as would effect this object which would be rendered more instructive by the numerous documents on the progress of the works in every branch of the service which are in my possession.

But the directors needed the money too badly, so they would not agree to the suggestion. The shield was sold for scrap, like its predecessor, and raised £900.

The paraphernalia of the tunnel's construction were steadily dismantled and removed and the tunnel was made ready for the foot passengers who would use it: it was paved and tiled throughout. Permanent staircases and landings were built in the whitewashed shafts, and pumps installed to deal with the small amount of continuing infiltration. There were problems with leaks in the tiny gap that had been left between the tunnel and the shaft which took a couple of months to correct and it was not until

August 1842 that the Wapping shaft was fitted out. Sightseers were then admitted for the first time to the tunnel's northern end.

Marc should have been able to relax now that what he called 'my arduous enterprise' was coming to an end. Instead, the strain of having to argue with the directors about all the relatively minor details that remained took its toll, and on 7th November he suffered a stroke which paralysed his right side. Isambard once more took on the responsibility for the engineering.

By March 1843 Marc was well enough to resume an active interest in affairs and that month's annual general meeting of shareholders voted him 'cordial thanks and congratulations . . . for the distinguished talent and energy and perseverance evinced by him in the design and construction and completion of the Thames Tunnel, a work unprecedented in the annals of science and ingenuity and exhibiting a triumph of genius over physical difficulties declared by some of the most enlightened men of the time to be insurmountable .'

And on 25th March 1843, the tunnel admitted its first penny-paying pedestrian.

THE GRAND OPENING

Marc had objected to the tunnel opening on this day, as it was a Saturday and 'Saturday night is the most disorderly time of the whole week', but was overruled by the directors. Early on that morning the visitors began to arrive in Rotherhithe, on foot, by coach , on horseback and by boat. A printing press had been lowered into the tunnel and *The Royal Thames Tunnel Paper* was being turned out for sale. By early afternoon, the crowds could be held back no longer and they stampeded down the spiral stairways, long before the official opening. This started at 4 o'clock with a cannon firing and the band of the Fusilier Guards striking up *See the Conquering Hero Comes!* The guests, led by Marc and his directors entered the shaft and descended down to the tunnel, walked to Wapping, then descended again and returned to Rotherhithe. At six o' clock the public were officially admitted, and in its first twenty-four hours 50,000 people had paid to enter. In the first ten days, 100,000 had entered. The following weekend – Easter – the crowds were unmanageable, with over

The opening procession, with Marc behind the union flag, waving his hat

10,000 people an hour coming into the tunnel. By 11th July – fifteen weeks and three days since opening – the total number of pedestrians reached one million.

Marc was away from London on 26th July 1843 when, with little warning, as was apparently her custom, Queen Victoria suddenly decided to pay a visit by royal barge to see the tunnel. It was her husband, Prince Albert, who had launched the *Great Britain* and he had returned so full of admiration for the mighty ship built by Isambard that the Queen decided it was time to see for herself the great achievement of his father.

She and Prince Albert and their small entourage, which included the Duke of Saxe-Coburg and Gotha, Princess Clementine and Lord Byron, were met by a party of tunnel company directors. Thomas Page, the resident engineer, stood in for Marc and walked at the Queen's side from Wapping to Rotherhithe and back. To him she expressed her admiration for the tunnel, adding: 'I had hoped Mr Brunel would be here'. Marc, too, when he heard of the royal visit, regretted his absence, but he had not received word in time to return. 'Otherwise', he wrote to the tunnel company secretary, 'I should certainly have gone up to receive Her Majesty in my own domains '. However, the Queen told Page that this was in fact her second visit – she'd seen the tunnel under construction when she was the little known Princess Victoria, an event not even recorded in Marc's diary.

A contemporary illustration shows the Royal Party alighting from the royal barge at Wapping. An interesting detail is the scaffolding on Irving & Brown's Coal wharf (top right) – erected to deal with the subsidence caused by the sinking of the Wapping shaft and for which the Thames Tunnel Company had to pay compensation.

ABOVE
Marc acknowledging the cheers of the crowds on the opening day

RIGHT
Queen Victoria and Prince Albert arriving at Wapping to visit the tunnel

The Celebrated Tunnel

To cross under a river via a kind of subterranean bridge rather than over it in the normal fashion was a truly miraculous concept for the Victorians and the excitement it caused is reflected in the quantity of commemorative items produced. Most of these commemoratives appeared after the tunnel was completed, but some printed souvenirs were produced almost as soon as construction began. Some were produced by independent publishers and printers, and some by the Thames Tunnel Company itself, anxious to keep public interest in the project, particularly during the seven-year stoppage of work.

Shortly after the ground-breaking ceremony in March 1825, an enterprising Kennington publisher, T. Brown, exploited the tunnel's 'optical' qualities and produced a peepshow. Published in June 1825, it came in a slipcase in cream or green or turquoise and when pulled out and opened the tunnel could be viewed in three dimensions in all its hoped-for future glory, brightly lit and filled with fine horse-drawn vehicles, stagecoaches, laden wagons and gaily-clad pedestrians. Brown's idea was taken up enthusiastically by others and dozens of peepshows appeared over the next thirty years, almost until the moment the tunnel was converted into a railway tunnel. The early peepshows are extremely fine. Some of them are double shows with two views: one of the river and its ships, the other of the tunnel beneath; some even include the tunnelling shield with the men at work in it. When the tunnel finally opened, a particularly splendid one appeared, showing a procession of dignitaries, a brass band playing lustily and Marc himself joyously waving his top hat. Many of them bear multi-lingual captions to appeal to an international public and they could be bought not only at the tunnel but also in shops in London (C. Essex & Co., of Gloster Street, for example), as far away as Leicester's Pantheon Bazaar and undoubtedly even farther afield. Alas, almost nothing is known about their makers.

An alternative to the peepshow was a 'Protean View' or 'transformation'. This was a lithograph printed on thin paper with a second view pasted behind. When the transformation was held up to the light or set it in a viewing frame, the front image would disappear, revealing the hidden image behind. In some the tunnel 'transformed' into Queen Victoria's coronation procession and some 'transformed' from a snow scene or Lake Windermere into the tunnel. Others were simpler, with just the tunnel and a sheet of tissue paper pasted on the back but when held up, the gas-lamps in the Tunnel would suddenly light up and shine brightly.

In March 1827, when visitors were first admitted to view the works, the Tunnel Company provided them with a guidebook with a text written by Marc himself (updated when necessary) and a set of good illustrations, most of them drawn by members of the engineering team. In pocket-sized format, these informative little books were issued and re-issued with extraordinary frequency, sometimes as often as three or four times a year, right up to 1862. They were also translated into the major European languages, including Norwegian and Dutch, and after 1835 there were American editions.

In May 1828, shortly before the seven-year stoppage, the Company began to issue handsome broadsheets. These bore a descriptive text (which again would be frequently updated) and illustrations of the tunnel and shield. They included details of opening times and public transport links and were reassuring in tone because they were, after all, enticing people to visit to a building site: 'The Archway is lighted with oil gas; the work is dry and warm, and the descent by a large staircase, and perfectly easy to ascend and descend', and people continued to flock to Rotherhithe. This endless flow of publicity material ensured that the tunnel remained in the forefront of everyone's mind while Marc was negotiating with the Government for further funds to complete it.

THE TUNNEL IN USE

Within a year more than two million people had paid their pennies and experienced the thrill of walking under the river. And there were other attractions to tempt visitors. In 1853, a German tourist, Max Schlesinger, wrote, "As we descend, stray bits of music greet our ears. Arrived at the bottom of the shaft there is the double pathway opening before us, and looking altogether dry, comfortable and civilised, for there are plenty of gas lights... As we proceed the music becomes more clear and distinct and here it is: a miniature exhibition of English industrial skill. It is an Italian organ played by a perfect doll of a Lilliputian steam-engine. That engine grinds the organ from morning till night; it gives us various pieces without any compunction or political scruples. *The*

Poster for the tunnel entertainments

Marseillaise, German waltzes, the Hungarian *Rakowzy March*, *Rule Britannia*, *Yankee Doodle*,etc. does this marvellous engine grind out of the organ."

There were also refreshments and, more importantly, a mass of souvenirs to purchase. The American novelist, Nathanial Hawthorne, described "an arched corridor of apparently interminable length, all along the extent of this corridor, in little alcoves, there are stalls or shops, kept principally by women, who, as you approach, are seen though the dusk offering for sale views of the Tunnel, put up with a little magnifying glass, in cases of Derbyshire spar; also cheap jewelry and multifarious trumpery".

Much of this 'trumpery' survives: cheroot cases, snuffboxes, pincushions, needle-cases, thimbles, little sewing-boxes, handkerchiefs, mugs and beakers in pottery and horn, children's plates, fine glass goblets, paperweights, shells, splendid gin flasks with the front moulded into the form of the Wapping entrance and many other weird and wonderful knick-knacks such as miniature muskets or spinning tops. Some bear only the words, 'Bought in the Thames Tunnel' or 'A present from the Thames Tunnel' (and after the Queen's visit 'The Royal Thames Tunnel') but others show the tunnel in cross-

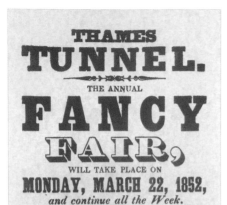

section, displaying the handsome double horseshoe-shaped arches and the grand stairways, or in sectional elevation with the river above. Hawthorne was describing what is now called a peep-egg, with a magnifying glass in the top (some have several views on a revolving spindle) and of course any amount of prints could be bought. All this contributed a much-needed £450 a year and more to the cash-strapped Thames Tunnel Company.

Some of the stall-holders are known. The enterprising Mr. W. Griffin, maker of coins and medals, caused a flurry of attention in the *Pictorial Times* in 1844 when a group of Ojibwa Indians *'halted at a stall, where bright medallions bearing the likeness of Mr. Brunel were offered for sale, [and] the owner Mr. Griffin liberally gave each of these novel visitors specimens of the showy memorials…When the party reached the Surrey side, they proceeded a short way up the staircase, and one of the 'braves' having received a duplicate medal, took it into his head to acknowledge the boisterous attention of the crowd below by throwing down in the midst the superfluous medal. A scramble ensued, which so much amused the whole party, that the first Indian's example was followed by all; and Mr. Griffin coming forward with a copious supply of the shiny pieces of metal, a metallic shower ensued'.*

J.V. Quick occupied Stand 47. He was a printer and publisher who had been producing such items as gas-lighters' annual Christmas poems from various premises in north London but was swift to cash in on the Tunnel's popularity, setting up a printing press from which he issued souvenir broadsheets, first to commemorate the opening and then to mark the Queen's visit later in the year. Each has an illustration and descriptive text surmounted with the proud words, "Printed by Authority, 76 feet below high-water mark" (one impressed owner wrote on his, "I saw this printed"). Another of Quick's broadsheets could be cut out and assembled at home to make a peepshow, one panel of which showed Quick at work at his press.

Much the most successful of the stall-holders was the printer and publisher, Bondy Azulay, who described himself as a "Perspective View Manufacturer", that is, a maker of peepshows. He occupied counters 27, 41 and 62, of which "Counter 41, for the sale of views of the tunnel, is exactly under the centre of the River Thames, and consequently the lowest part of the structure". He seems to have set up his business in the tunnel about the time it opened and to have continued there almost to 1862. His peepshows were cheap and cheerful and immensely popular, with a crude charm all their own. They came with a sheet of figures to be cut out and pasted on to the panels of the show, which could then be coloured to your own satisfaction. However, Azulay had many other tempting items, such as 'Engravings on Enamel', which were heavy white glazed cards illustrating one or other of the curving staircases and entrance arches in black or 'bronzed' (gilt). He also sold writing paper, each sheet headed with a view of the Tunnel, and perhaps it was from him too that tiny wafers could be bought, colour-embossed with the twin arches with which to seal an envelope, or even a 'Spell for Love' surmounted by a circular view of the Wapping entrance, which prescribes "12 ounces of Dislike, 1 pound of Resolution" and other "drugs...to be had of the Apothecary at the House of Understanding, next door to Reason in Prudent Street in the Parish of Contentment". Azulay even used 'Thames Tunnel' as his imprint, issuing 'A Grand Panorama of London and the River Thames' under this name, which could be purchased either at one of his counters or ordered by post.

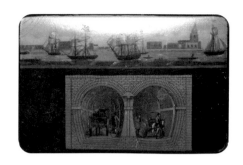

OPPOSITE
Poster for the Fancy Fair

ABOVE AND LEFT
Commemorative snuff boxes

71

The Fate of the Tunnel

A nurseryware commemorative plate

OPPOSITE
A north-bound train on the East London
line in 1870

In about 1851 an exceptionally fine peepshow by an unknown maker shows it all
abustle with crowds seething round stalls overflowing with brightly coloured
wares. The following year the first Thames Tunnel Fancy Fair was held, with tightwire
artists, fire eaters, sword swallowers, Ethiopian serenaders, Indian dancers, Chinese
singers, electricity, and Mr E. Green, the celebrated bottle pantomimic equilibrist. But
a decade later it was seedy and run down, a nocturnal haunt of tramps and drunks.
The tunnel had lost its appeal, its novelty dulled by the engineering wonders of the
railway age.

Marc Brunel's Thames Tunnel was a landmark in engineering which was to prove
an inspiration to succeeding generations of tunnellers. Unfortunately, like many other
pioneering projects, the tunnel showed the way, but failed to realise its original
objectives. The 40-ft wide spiral roadway approaches that would have allowed horse-
drawn traffic to use the tunnel were never built.

Although the discussion about them continued even after Marc's death,
the problem remained a circular one: the tunnel was not profitable so no-one
would venture to develop it any further, yet until the carriageways were built, the
tunnel never *would* be profitable. Furthermore, as a pedestrian subway in competition
with the ferry boars, it suffered from its long stairways – at Rotherhithe, over one
hundred stairs up and down, and at Wapping ninety-nine stairs each way.

1846 was to mark the third great investment boom in railways in the nineteenth
century, so, perhaps not surprisingly, in that year the use of the Thames Tunnel for
rail traffic was first mooted. Marc is said to have approved of the scheme, which
was being enthusiastically promoted by Benjamin Hawes, the then-chairman of
the Thames Tunnel Company. After a favourable recommendation by a House
of Lords committee, the East London Railway Company was incorporated by an
Act in May 1865. The company's remit was to build a line downstream of London
Bridge that would connect with all the railways entering London north and south
of the Thames. The East London Railway Company's prospectus of June 1865

claimed: 'The East London Railway will complete the Metropolitan system of railways recommended by the Joint Committee of both Houses of Parliament in the Session of 1864'.

The tunnel was sold to the East London Railway for £200,000 and was formally handed over on 25th September 1865. Operating between Wapping & Shadwell Station and New Cross, the East London Railway opened for public traffic on 7th December 1869. Sadly, the tunnel's architectural features were either obscured or obliterated.

After terminal financial difficulties the East London Railway was put into the hands of the receiver in 1878. Subsequently, the company's operations came under the control of the East London Railway Joint Committee, a regime which was to last from 1882 to 1949. On the night of 11th September 1940 high explosive and incendiary bombs set fire to buildings adjoining Wapping Station and the station's surface buildings were destroyed. Nevertheless, the railway continued to operate and during the period leading up to D-Day, vast quantities of armour and ammunition passed to the forward assembly areas through the tunnel, demonstrating the foresight shown by Ralph Dodd 142 years earlier with his vision of a 'grand uninterrupted line of communication in the south-east part of the Kingdom'.

When the railways of Britain were nationalised in 1948 the East London Railway became part of the London Transport railway system. Now well over a century and a half after its opening Marc Brunel's tunnel continues in daily use as a safe and dry thoroughfare under the Thames for passenger rail traffic on the busy London Overground.

SOLVING THE CROSSING PROBLEM

In 1869, forty-six years after the start of Marc's tunnel, another tunnel under the Thames was begun. Designed as a narrow gauge, cable-hauled railway with a single coach, the 'Tower Subway' was a long way indeed from the scale of Marc's ideas. It was opened in August 1870, but closed within months to re-open as a subway for pedestrians. It had given little relief to the traffic problem, and between 1874 and 1885, no fewer than thirty petitions were submitted to the Corporation of the City of London asking for a new bridge to be built.

In 1876 the Corporation set up a committee to review the possibilities for a new crossing east of London Bridge and in the next ten years it considered almost thirty

Marc in old age

proposals: for high-level bridges, low-level bridges, ferries and a tunnel, grandly presented as a 'sub-riverian arcade'.

Sir Horace Jones, the City Engineer, proposed a 'bascule' bridge ('bascule' being the French for 'see-saw'),: that is, a bridge divided into halves the adjoining tips of which would rise – and part – as their opposite ends sank. Its engines would be powered by steam. In 1885 Parliament passed the Act authorising the construction of Tower Bridge and work began the following year, carried out by Sir John Wolfe Barry, with the assistance of Isambard's son, Henry Marc Brunel, who supervised the calculations and details of the structure.

In the first year of the bridge's existence the river traffic was such that it was raised 6,160 times while by road an average of eight thousand horse-drawn vehicles and sixty thousand pedestrians crossed it daily. Had Marc been allowed to complete his tunnel, it could have coped quite happily with traffic on that scale, and Tower Bridge need never have been built. Magnificent though it was, Tower Bridge was never more than a compromise solution.

THE BRUNELS AFTER THE TUNNEL

The Thames Tunnel marked the end of Marc's professional career but he received considerable pleasure from the achievements of Isambard – so much so that attending the launch in Bristol of his son's revolutionary steamship *Great Britain* meant that he inadvertently missed the Queen's visit to the Thames Tunnel. Sadly, a second stoke hit him in 1845 and he was forced to withdraw from general society. He died on 12th December 1849, and was buried five days later in Kensal Green Cemetery. Within the decade he was joined by Isambard, worn out by the stress of creating the greatest steamship the world had ever seen, the *Great Eastern* (built just a few miles downstream of the tunnel) but not before he had created some of the greatest engineering works in the country. These included the Great Western Railway and the Royal Albert Bridge at Saltash. More modestly, he had even built his own Thames crossing, the Hungerford Suspension Bridge. This was dismantled in 1865 to make way for a new railway bridge but its chains were recycled to complete one of his earliest, but unfinished projects, the Clifton Suspension Bridge, where they still hang.

Isambard beside the launching chains of the *Great Eastern*

Where the Tunnel Led

Commemorative box

Tunnelling may have been mankind's first exercise in engineering. The reinforcement and extension of his home would have been an essential activity for a cave dweller and indeed the remains of Stone Age victims of tunnel collapses have been found, together with their tunnelling implements. Since then, the uses and requirements for tunnels have developed in accordance with society's needs, and now, tunnels are used for drainage, sewerage and the transport of water, gas, people and goods.

As a civil engineering activity, tunnelling can be divided into two categories: hard-rock tunnelling and soft-ground tunnelling. In hard-rock tunnelling the objective is to produce an opening – the tunnel – in what is usually a rock mass by breaking out and removing fragments of rock. Here, the main problem facing the engineer is the task of removing the rock to form the excavation. Once the excavation has been formed, how ever, it can usually support itself, providing the rock mass is reasonably uniform and homogeneous. By contrast, the excavation process in soft-ground tunnelling is usually easily accomplished, but the problem is to prevent the ground from collapsing into the tunnel.

Before Marc Brunel, soft-ground tunnelling was carried by hand, using spade, pick and shovel, followed by elaborate timbering to support the walls and roof of the excavation. Soft-ground tunnelling by these traditional methods was laborious and dangerous and certainly could not be carried out beneath the water-table in permeable strata. Brunel's pioneering achievement was to demonstrate that tunnels could be constructed in any soft ground, including the difficult and hazardous environments that prevailed under rivers, lakes and seas.

As we have seen, Brunel considered that his original design for a circular shield could not be implemented with the technology then available and therefore designed the rectangular shield which was used to construct the Thames Tunnel. As it turned out, the first shield in Brunel's patent of 1818 is more directly the ancestor of tunnelling shields as they developed than is his Thames Tunnel shield. In 1868, fifty years after Brunel's patent, Peter William Barlow, an engineer of some repute, patented his own ideas for a circular tunnelling shield. A year later, he was appointed engineer for the Tower Subway, although the man in charge of construction was James Henry Greathead, a young South African apprenticed to Barlow. The tunnelling shield for driving the Tower Subway was designed by Greathead, but was clearly inspired by Barlow's ideas.

The importance of the Tower Subway achievement bore a significance that extended far beyond the tunnel itself. Between 1896 and 1907 the deep tube tunnels of the London Underground were driven with what had become known as 'Greathead shields'. The idea of the cylindrical tunnel shield quickly spread abroad and other cities soon followed London's example in providing themselves with underground railways. Barlow and Greathead had demonstrated a safe and practicable method for soft-ground tunnelling which has served as a model for such tunnel construction all over the world up to the present day. The gigantic tunnel boring machines which have made possible such modern marvels as the Seikan, Channel, Crossrail and Thames Tideway Tunnels, can be seen to be the lineal descendants of Brunel's first shield design.

ABOVE
Commemorative carved horn beaker

LEFT
Commemorative engraved glass rummer

The Tunnel Today

Marc's Wapping shaft today still forms the entrance to Wapping Station on the East London Railway, now part of the London Overground The ticket hall contains a plaque to both Brunels, erected by London Underground. A lift shaft has been installed in the centre, but, although the original stairways have been taken away, it is still possible to descend and ascend the shaft by a spiralling stairway, as passengers had done in the mid-nineteenth century.

The tunnel itself begins at the end of the platforms, which are now decorated with details from nineteenth century prints celebrating the tunnel and its history. A major refurbishment in 1995 has enabled passengers to see the sixty arches between the north – and southbound tunnels much more easily, and the last four arches on the Rotherhithe side are preserved in their original condition.

Rotherhithe Station is modern and dates from the tunnel's incorporation into the tube system and the tunnel visible here is an extension built in 1865. From its platforms, the noise of lorries and cars can be heard as they descend to cross the river through the area's second tunnel, the Rotherhithe Tunnel, opened in 1908. At the bottom of the escalators is a plaque marking an International Landmark Site, one of only four in the country (and only 250 in the world), in recognition that this is the birthplace of modern urban transport. It was here that the Brunels, father and son, pioneered a method of tunnelling used in every tube system all over the world ever since. The plaque was erected by the Institution of Civil Engineers in Britain and the American Society of Civil Engineers on the tunnel's 150th birthday.

Marc's Rotherhithe shaft now stands in the middle of landscaped gardens stocked with shrubs and trees chosen by I.K. Brunel for his chateau in Watcombe in Devon. The shaft stood open to the skies until capped in the 1940s because of fears that the tunnel lights made a landmark for enemy aircraft. Externally, the rendered brickwork is part of an award winning fish sculpture by local children, working under the guidance of artist Liz Leyh. The choice of materials – found & recycled materials, and concrete – is a reference to Brunel's original construction, using fast drying Roman cement and

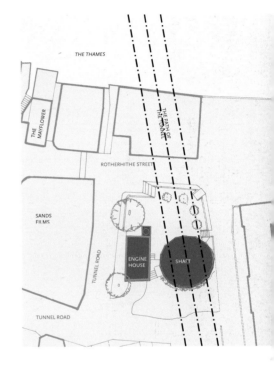

ABOVE
The area around the Rotherhithe shaft and The Brunel Museum today:
map by Barry Noon

OPPOSITE
The tunnel after the restoration in 1995

ABOVE
A peep-show of the tunnel, on display in The Brunel Museum

BELOW
Inside The Brunel Museum

OPPOSITE
Inside the Grand Entrance Hall

excavated clay, baked and re-cycled as bricks. On the south east face of the shaft is a bas relief design of the tunnelling shield, similar to that in the watercolour by Yates (see p. 32). The railings at the top carry a permanent installation showing Isambard's greatest industrial achievements.

Below the frieze, a doorway cut through the brickwork leads into an underground chamber half the size of Shakespeare's Globe. A reinforced concrete floor separates the tunnels from the upper gallery. The railway company removed the original wooden stairs long ago, and a new staircase casts a shadow across its outline, still visible on the soot encrusted walls of Brunel's Grand Entrance Hall. On the 210th anniversary of Isambard Kingdom Brunel's birth, the site was designated a National Historic Landmark, and in November 2016 the Grand Entrance Hall was opened as a gallery, theatre and performance space by HRH Prince Edward The Earl of Wessex KG GCVO. There was entertainment here in Brunel's day, and today, once again, the chamber echoes with applause. Music, opera, concerts and theatre have returned to the Eighth Wonder of the World. The acoustics are remarkable.

To the south is the 'Ship of Blueprints', an installation by local children working with artist Martin Cottis. Twenty tall backed seats, in Cor-ten steel, ring a table set with a hundred blue tiles engraved by local children. The tiles illustrate various Brunel projects, from tunnels and bridges to railways and ships.

To the north, a brick paved square overlooks the river, with benches designed in the shape of three famous bridges designed by Isambard. On Maidenhead Bridge, the lowest flattest brick arch in the world, children have made a mosaic of railway lines. On the Royal Albert Bridge children have made the Iron Duke, a broad gauge locomotive. On Hungerford Bridge children's enamelled portraits appear on copper sheets. The bridges won an award in 2005. Overlooking them is a mural from a painting by Marc Brunel, acquired with the help of the Art Fund.

During construction of the tunnel, thousands of gallons of water poured in every hour. An engine and boiler on top of the shaft pumped the water out, but when the tunnel was opened to the public the engine and boiler were moved into a purpose-built engine house. The engine was broken up, and for a long time the building was as a store until it fell into disrepair. In 1973 a charity was set up to restore the engine house, by then scheduled as an Ancient Monument, and in 1980 the newly roofed building opened to the public. This building now houses The Brunel Museum, commemorating the tunnel, the Brunels and the men who built it.

The Brunel Museum

BELOW
The tunnel entrance at Wapping today

Every day The Brunel Museum organises guided heritage boat tours, from the centre of town: by Thames Clipper down the river and over the Thames Tunnel, then by train, through the tunnel, and into the underground chamber. Visitors travel under three Brunel bridges to reach the launch ways of IK Brunel's last great ship on the Isle of Dogs. The launch ways are now scheduled as an Ancient Monument. The piers of IK Brunel's Hungerford Bridge remain, but the chains now span the gorge at Clifton in Bristol. Blackfriars Railway Bridge and Tower Bridge (Horace Jones), were built by IK Brunel's son Henry Marc Brunel, with business partner John Wolfe Barry. The Brunel family boasts a dynasty of engineers, and most of their works are in London.

Locally, The Brunel Museum has developed close ties with the community and its audience. The Museum has been responsible for the installations and other developments at the Rotherhithe end of the tunnel. A charity largely reliant on volunteers, the Museum runs many activities, including theatre, concerts and recitals, summer play schemes for young people and artists' residencies when entertainments are devised and performed in the spirit of the Thames Tunnel Fancy Fair of 1852. As well as heritage boat tours, the charity also organises guided tours of the tunnel by train, and even by foot, when planned engineering works require the line to be closed to trains.

The charity is proud to have received The Queen's Award for Voluntary Service.

Bibliography

BEAVER, PATRICK *A History of Tunnels* (Peter Davies, 1972).

BRINDLE, STEVEN *Brunel: the man who built the world* (Weidenfield & Nicolson, 2005).

CLEMENTS, PAUL *Marc Isambard Brunel* (Longmans Green and Co. Ltd., 1970).

GRAY, ROBERT *A History of London* (Hutchinson, 1978).

JONES, BRONWEN, ED. *The Tunnel – the Channel and Beyond* (Ellis Horwood, Ltd., 1987).

KIEK, JONATHAN *Everybody's Historic London: a history and guide* (Quiller Press, 1984).

LAMPE, DAVID *The Tunnel: the story of the world's first tunnel under a navigable river dug beneath the Thames 1824-42* (Harrap, 1963).

LEE, CHARLES E *The East London Line and Thames Tunnel* (London Transport, 1976).

MINDELL, RUTH AND JONATHAN *Bridges over the Thames* (Blandford Press, 1985).

PUDNEY, JOHN *Brunel and His World* (Thames & Hudson, 1974).

ROLT, L.T.C. *Isambard Kingdom Brunel* (Penguin Books, 1989).

TRENCH, RICHARD AND HILLMAN, ELLIS *London under London* (John Murray, 1985).

WEST, GRAHAM *Innovation and the Rise of the Tunnelling Industry* (Cambridge University Press, 1988).

Acknowledgements

The Brunel Museum wishes to thank the following for permission to reproduce illustrations: The National Portrait Gallery, pages 15, 18 and 60; The Guildhall Library, London, pages 10, 21, 22 and 84; The Ironbridge Gorge Museum, page 40; The South London Gallery, page 32; Bryan Jones, pages 56, 59, 71, 72, 76, 77 and 78; Heini Schneebeli, page 80; and private individuals, pages 27, 33, 34, 35, 36, 38 (lower), 39, 44, 48 and 74. All other illustrations are from The Brunel Museum collection.

ABOVE
The award winning Fancy Fair Summer playscheme in the Museum Gardens 2005

OVERLEAF
The entrance to the tunnel as originally planned: a view from the carriageway never built, by B. Dixie, 1836